17/6

D₂

GROWTH TO FREEDOM

Derek Miller, M.D.

GROWTH TO FREEDOM

The Psychosocial Treatment of Delinquent Youth

With an introduction by
FRANK FOSTER
Director of the Borstal After-Care Association

TAVISTOCK PUBLICATIONS

First published in Great Britain in 1964
by Tavistock Publications (1959) Limited
11 New Fetter Lane, London E.C.4
Printed in Great Britain
in 12 point Bembo
by Fletcher & Son Ltd, Norwich

Contents

Author's Preface

THIS BOOK is about the treatment of some of society's cripples, young institutionalized deprived delinquents. When emotional crippling occurs the process by which human beings give to one another is interrupted, and vicious circles of mutual attack and withdrawal tend ultimately to be created between the individual, his family, and the society in which he lives. His relationship to himself becomes equally unsatisfactory. Only when these processes are interrupted can he start to realize his potentiality as a human being. Crippling may ultimately become irreversible, and certainly a damaged individual cannot be helped unless all the determinants that helped to create the trouble are assessed as to their relative importance and then dealt with appropriately. Our society is so constructed that in effect adolescence provides a last chance for self-realization. If this is lost it is difficult, if not impossible, either to find new opportunities or, even if they are found, for human beings to be sufficiently plastic to take them. This is particularly pertinent for the maladjusted adolescent; it almost appears with some people that if help is not given during adolescence, its application thereafter becomes almost fruitless.

Society as a whole tends not to value expertise, and one of the reasons why people and organizations are not successfully helped to be more productive is that attempts at this are often applied either in a highly limited way or with a shot-gun technique. It is as if, to use a medical analogy, fever is treated without a study of its aetiology; either by the use of aspirin or by having the individual take all the known antibiotics. In such situations the cure may be worse than the disease.

This study of ways of helping delinquents to become less anti-social and more productive is based on the premise that aetiology

ix

must be understood and then the individual treated in as expert a way as possible. Merely to blame the badness of others and to lament its effects can only be sterile; that is, in effect, the technique used by the inadequate organization or individual to justify their present parlous state.

Broadly speaking, there is a private and a public causality to delinquency. This means that help can be effective only if a therapeutic approach is both psychological, helping the individual with himself and in his immediate relationship to others; and sociological, studying and attempting to change the relevant processes in society at large and in the immediate community. It is necessary to consider the past only in so far as it affects the present. The aim should be to have a richer future in terms both of the individual's emotional life and of what he is able to achieve.

This is the general approach which is used in this pilot study with delinquents; it would appear to be valid for all maladjustment, both of the individual and of larger social organizations, but whether, if the techniques were applied with larger populations, the results would be precisely the same is an open question.

A team of people worked to produce this effort, as is obvious from the text, and it is invidious to single out any one person for special mention. The project was created because people of similar ideas met together and were able to work cohesively. Economic resources were freely provided by a family trust, but as people, its members gave us much more than financial support, for they showed a sustained interest and involvement that were highly constructive. To them we owe our thanks.

The manuscript was read and helpful comments made by the trustees of the project, and by Mr. Frank Foster, Mr. H. Taylor, Mrs. Dunnachie, and Dr. J. D. Sutherland. Mr. W. MacMillan helped in the collection of the figures for the statistical work. The patience of Miss E. Stant in retyping the manuscript through numerous drafts must be acknowledged. Mrs. E. Rosenfeld was personally most helpful to the author in the formulation of many of the concepts and ideas that appear in the text.

D.M.

Introduction

THIS BOOK derives from the first two and a half years of the life
of a project that is the product of many years of concern with the
problems of the homeless and institutionalized youthful offender
and the profound realization of failure to make any vital contribution to the solution of these problems.

As the assistant warden of a boys' hostel catering mainly for
what were then known as 'poor law' boys; as a member of the
staff of a home for what would now be known as deprived and
maladjusted boys, again drawn mainly from poor law institutions
and local authority homes; for eighteen years as a probation officer
and since 1949 as Director of Borstal After-Care, I was constantly
made aware of the difficulties experienced by this deprived
minority in trying to make an adjustment to the demands of
normal society.

During these years I had ample scope for exploring the behaviour and attitudes of this group and, on becoming Director of
Borstal After-Care, I welcomed the opportunity of making a
wider, as distinct from a purely personal, contribution towards
solving some of the problems of the deprived youthful offender.

My thinking at this time was based upon the premise that,
because the homeless boy had never known real family life, his
primary need was to become a member of a small family group
where some substitute for all he had missed in life could be provided; so, rather naïvely, I conceived the best method of meeting
this need was to place him in homely lodgings where he could
live as one of a family. It became the policy of Borstal After-Care,
therefore, to make arrangements, wherever possible, to place
homeless boys in family-type lodgings, and only when these were
not available or where the boy concerned was for any of a number

of reasons totally unsuited for such a placement, or in an emergency, to have recourse to hostels or lodging houses, and then only as a temporary measure. At the same time we created a special unit within the division charged with the duty of exploring the needs of the homeless boy, making long-term plans for his resettlement, and providing the most favourable background possible for him on release. In some cases these methods proved effective, in certain cases strikingly so, but in all too many cases the most carefully made plans proved abortive.

We were faced with these facts. We could define the deprived offender, we could describe him, we were familiar with his attitudes, we knew how he was likely to behave in given circumstances, we could make arrangements for his reception and resettlement on release that seemed tailor-made to meet his particular needs and yet, time and again, we proved powerless to influence the depressingly familiar course of events. Repeatedly, boys in these circumstances failed at a time of real or imagined crisis. For my own part I felt that after thirty years of trying to help the deprived and homeless boy I knew little more about him and was hardly a whit more effective in my efforts to help him than I had been at the beginning. I could say with Antonio 'I have considered well his loss of time and how he cannot be a perfect man not being tried and tutored in the world' but I lacked Antonio's simple remedy; I had no court of Milan.

Alongside the facts leading to this sense of failure was, of course, the realization that there was no convincing evidence that any of the current methods of treating offenders were outstandingly successful and, although new techniques had been evolved and applied, none was demonstrably more successful than any other. No real progress was being made.

Stated in its simplest terms, this was the problem. The over-institutionalized delinquent (and research by Dr. Roger Hood conducted at my invitation suggested that anything more than four and a half years' residence in institutions could be defined as 'over-institutionalization') faces outside life with totally inadequate resources. He is socially inept and inexperienced: his inability to form satisfying relationships is demonstrated in his attitude towards adults, whether at work or socially; towards girls and women; towards any aspect of authority; and, save in a tenuous way, towards his peers. He is profoundly distrustful of other people, especially of adults, and needs constant reassurance about the genuineness of their motives and of their regard for him. He is extremely egocentric, yet at the same time not really self-regarding. He is emotionally deprived and invariably emotionally disturbed to a greater or lesser degree. Additionally, he has a degree of criminal experience and, at a time of what seems to him intolerable stress, he readily turns to some overt self-damaging demonstration, usually of a criminal nature. How, I was forced to ask myself, in view of the comparative failure of all we had attempted up to now, could we really help such a boy?

It was, perhaps, George who first directed my thoughts in what might prove to have been the right direction. He was a homeless ex-borstal boy in whom I had taken a personal interest. Work within his capacity and comfortable lodgings with a friendly working-class family had been arranged for him. He had spent his home leave with them and seemed happy there. No serious problems were expected following his release. A fortnight after his release he came to see me. His opening words were, 'Please, Mr. Foster, send me back to borstal.'

He went on to explain his situation in the following terms, 'I know you meant well when you sent me to my lodgings. They're kind people there but I know nothing about living in a place like that. I've always been used to a dining-hall and a recreation room big enough to move about in. At my lodgings there's the fire-place here and the table there and the sofa and the sideboard and the piano and the chairs, all in a little space and there isn't room to move about in, not even room to swing your arms. I've already knocked the teapot off the table twice. Can't you send me to a hostel where I can sort of get settled in? Or send me back to borstal? I was happy there.' Leaving me to digest this for a few moments, he then added, 'You needn't be bothered about my getting into trouble again. I shan't do that. If anything goes wrong I've always got you to come and talk to. I shan't do anything silly.' He made it perfectly clear, although he was quite unconscious of doing so, that if he did come to see me about any problems he had a pathetic faith (at that time unearned as far as I was concerned) that I should come up with the answer.

If George described the nature of our problem it was Ted who stressed its reality and urgency. He, too, was utterly homeless and without known relatives. He, too, was found lodgings, in his case with a sympathetic and paternal landlord. One day he came to see us and talked for a long time. He clearly had something that he urgently wanted to talk about, but despite encouragement he left without saying what was on his mind. The next day we heard that he had returned to his lodgings, gone to his room, and, late at night, taken the greater part of a bottle of phenobarbitone tablets. As he was dying, he tried to write down what he had wanted to say, but, as unconsciousness overcame him, his writing became a meaningless scrawl. Once more we had failed.

Clearly the so much more than orthodox support and help that such boys as George and Ted needed just did not exist. How could they respond successfully to the demands of a substitute home if they had no idea what home life meant or what a home was? How could they make a satisfactory adjustment to normal life if they had to make the attempt in an emotional vacuum? How could they make satisfactory relationships if they had no experiences of a continuing and satisfying relationship? Other questions presented themselves. How could we destroy, and with what could we replace, the 'we–they' concept that seemed built into the make-up of the institutionalized boy? What were the destructive factors in the institutional situation and how could they be avoided? What more effective weapon could be found than the individual casework support that was plainly inadequate in the majority of such cases? Did borstal training serve any constructive purpose with the deprived delinquent?

I had no faith in the concept of a hostel as simply a half-way house. This seemed merely to add one more rejection to the lives of the already too-often rejected, and experience shows that its long-term value is suspect. I had no faith in any project depending for its success upon the personality of a single outstanding person. Such are apt to die with their founder and are not replicable. We were seeking something both effective and capable of widespread use, irrespective of the value to the project of any one person.

My thoughts had been developing along these lines for some time when a charitable trust declared its willingness to support a project likely to make a positive contribution to the reclamation of the offender, and I then crystallized them in the following terms and it was in some such terms that they were submitted to the trustees.

The lack of a home is only the most obvious disability under which the homeless delinquent suffers. Often he has spent a lifetime in one institution or another and because of this he is highly dependent, lacks social sense, is rootless and lacks attachment, and often has personality problems of a profoundly disturbing nature.

In the institutional setting he is usually reasonably happy and contented, well behaved and biddable, and, because of his passive acceptance of the organized life of the institution, his real lack of ability to cope with and his lack of experience of the situations thrown up by ordinary life outside the institution are not revealed. The tightly structured community masks his inadequacies. These are revealed on release when his pitiful efforts to deal with unfamiliar situations lead him to stumble from one crisis to another and involve him in many more or less serious setbacks and often in a dreary round of reconviction, committal, and release.

The ordinary hostel is merely a palliative for this type of boy. At its worst it provides a temporary and not very salubrious shelter; at its best it provides a homely supportive sanctuary. It does little to prepare him to face and deal with the basic problems he will meet on leaving the security of the hostel or to teach him to recognize and cope with them. His last condition is almost as bad as his first.

Introduction

The policy of placing homeless ex-borstal boys in lodgings has similarly not proved sufficiently effective. Apart from the intermittent support given by the supervising officer, and sometimes by his landlord and landlady, the boy is largely dependent upon his own slender resources and, although in many cases this works out satisfactorily, it does not provide the continued support so necessary to the grossly deprived boy.

The need, then, is for a hostel of a special kind with material and staffing resources in excess of those usually available.

The project can best be described under the following headings.

1. The Therapeutic Community.
2. The Supporting Role.
3. The Outpatients' Unit.
4. The Home.
5. Research.
6. Training.

1. The Therapeutic Community. The therapeutic role of the hostel would be based upon the group. Boys would be expected to take part in regular group counselling sessions. As the ultimate purpose of the hostel is to fit the boy for life outside, the group would be outward- as well as inward-looking and it would be expected to make a contribution to the life of the hostel, to the local community, and to the larger community as a group. If the group's activities revealed the need of any member for individual therapy, that need would be met, if at a simple level, by the hostel staff and, if at a deeper level, by an outside clinic.

2. The Supporting Role. It is absolutely imperative that most deprived boys should receive support for a long time, sometimes for several years. The supporting element of the hostel should be extended not only to the boys but to the people with whom they are ultimately found lodgings. I visualize, therefore, that before a boy is moved into lodgings the potential hosts would be seen by the social worker, invited to the hostel, and

shown the whole structure of the scheme. Both they and the
boy would know that they could turn to the hostel for advice
and guidance, and, in addition to the support the boy received
from his supervising officer, he would receive support as outlined
below under heading 4. Long-term follow-up should be possible
under this scheme, and a boy would be able to rely upon support
as long as he needed it.

  3. The Outpatients' Unit. I would expect the hostel to provide
some services for those deprived boys who, although not resident in the hostel, could derive benefit from its supportive and
therapeutic element. For this purpose accommodation would
be provided for group meetings and private talks with non-
residents. The purpose of the hostel is to meet *all* the needs of
the deprived boy and I visualize the Outpatients' Unit (although
we should not use this name) as being vital to the welfare of the
non-resident and ex-resident and, of course, to research and
training under headings 5 and 6.

  4. The Home. It is essential that the hostel should be a home
in the full sense of the word, a place to which a boy could
invite his friends, a place in which he could do all the things he
would normally do at home, a bit of wood-work, repairing his
motor-cycle and so on, and above all a place to which he could
return. I would expect it therefore to have a room large enough
to hold a wedding reception in, one comfortable enough to do
a bit of courting in, and I would expect it to have a yard for
doing odd jobs on cycles and motor-cycles and to have a work-
shop. I would expect old boys to bring their girls to the hostel
and probably to marry from the hostel.

  5. Research. Although we are familiar with the manifestations
of the deprived boy's difficulties, we know too little about dealing with them. The hostel should provide, with its skilled staff,
consultants, group methods, and liberal atmosphere and attitude,
unique opportunities for exploring the mentality and social
orientation of the deprived boy. These opportunities should
be exploited to the full and a research programme under skilled
direction should be a normal part of the function of the hostel.

6. Training. Similarly, I would expect to be able to use the hostel in a training programme for after-care workers and probably borstal housemasters. The possibilities here would only reveal themselves with the passage of time.

General. As the aim is to make this a home, I would not expect to see sharp divisions between staff and boys. I would expect visiting staff, social workers and consultants, for instance, to take their meals with the boys and, although resident staff would have to be able to live their own private lives, I would expect them to take certain meals with the boys.

I would expect the hostel to play a part in the life of the local community and would therefore expect local people (employers, for instance) from time to time to join in the life of the hostel. I would not, however, expect it to be a show place visited by all and sundry or to be the happy hunting ground of cranks. The residents should never be able to feel that they were exhibits, so that visitors should come only as family guests. This would not only preserve the true character of the place as a home but allow the boys to develop social grace. Also, in keeping with the aim to preserve the homelike character of the place, it should not be known as a hostel; some more suitable name must be used.

The scheme would call for the services of a consultant psychiatrist with considerable experience in group work and for one (at least) of the staff to be a trained social worker.

Cost. I visualize the scheme as being initially a five-year project and its total cost over that period being in the region of £50,000. This, of course, would include the cost of the property, which, at the end of the five-year period, would be a considerable capital asset.

It was to the scheme thus presented that the trustees promised their financial support. As will be seen later, they gave more than that. Once the parent trust had approved the project, events moved swiftly. They first considered the scheme in February 1960. By July 1960 a special trust had been formed, four trustees had been appointed, the house had been bought, and plans for the considerable and necessary repairs and adaptations were well advanced. By the end of the year repairs and decorations were completed. We considered that painting and decorating the house would form a valuable training exercise for borstal boys following a vocational training course, and invited the nearest borstal to undertake this work. This invitation was accepted, and a group of boys, travelling to the house daily, not only carried out all the internal decorations but designed the colour schemes and chose the wallpapers. Apart from being a useful training exercise, the boys and their instructors were delighted to be taking an active part in the project, the purpose of which was explained to them. By January 1961 the place was furnished, the warden and matron were in post, and, owing largely to their efforts, all the details that make a home were completed. Between 19 and 23 January the first four boys arrived. The adventure had begun.

At this point it is necessary to examine the structure of the project, for if it is in any way successful it will be of lasting value only if the reasons for its success are understood and are capable of reproduction in other similar projects. It has already been said that the support given by the supervisor in orthodox supervision is too intermittent. In addition, it is not readily available at times of crisis nor is it sufficiently long term. Moreover, the supervisor often lacks sufficient time to work through the anti-authority phase of the boy's feelings and thus is unable to earn the boy's trust to the degree necessary to ensure that the boy will turn to him in times of crisis. The individual-support aspect of the project was therefore based upon the concept of a therapeutic team, the most closely involved members being the resident staff, the psychiatrist, and the supervisor, a senior member of the staff of Borstal After-Care. Other members of the staff of Borstal After-Care were involved and were known to the boys, though not in the same intimate way as was the supervisor. Although in the early days the roles played by the members of the team were ill defined, especially to the boys, a pattern soon evolved. No titles such as 'warden' or 'matron' were used, nor were unrealistic euphemisms employed. The present warden, for instance, is addressed as Mrs. D., the assistant warden by his Christian name, the psychiatrist (no attempt has been made to hide the fact that he is a psychiatrist) and the supervisor by their surnames as Doctor and Mister. All that is false has been avoided. The boys know that, although they elect to go to the home, are there voluntarily, and may leave when they wish, they are under the statutory supervision of the supervisor under the same conditions as any other ex-borstal boy.

The affairs of the home are directed by a house committee which meets monthly. The members are the four trustees, two other members who have been associated with the work of the parent trust for many years, the Director of Borstal Administration, the warden and assistant warden, the supervisor, the psychiatrist, and myself. Although the house committee meetings are naturally concerned with the administration of the home, they really have the character rather of case discussions, and the members follow the progress of the boys with real insight and knowledge. The house committee is a source of tremendous support to the therapeutic team. The value of the therapeutic team has been demonstrated in four main ways.

1. It appears to have destroyed or abated the 'we–they' concept. There is in the exercise no anonymous and threatening 'they' liable to capricious and arbitrary action. The members of the team are known to the boys as recognizable names and faces, they are known to be approachable and accepting, and they are ultimately accepted as being reasonable.

2. The numerical strength of the team ensures the constant and massive support that is so clearly needed. Any boy may confidently seek understanding, guidance, reassurance, and support at literally any hour of the day or night, and may command that which is appropriate to his immediate need. The fact that emergency help is not now demanded as frequently as in the early days of the project suggests among other reasons that its very availability often gives the reassurance that is needed without its having actually to be called upon.

3. The presence of the team has helped the boys to cope with crisis, and for a brief spell, quite chaotic staff conditions within the home, so that when, for instance, a temporary warden whom the boys liked was taken ill and rushed to hospital, his sudden withdrawal was compensated for by the other members of the team. Indeed, with this team support, the boys have survived potentially destructive situations in a manner far exceeding our expectations. The home is deliberately located not far from the psychiatrist's home so that he has been readily available when the boys have needed him. The boys' dependence upon him or any other member of the team has not been so great, however, as to prevent its being understood by the boys and so absorbed by other members during annual leave or other absences.

4. Through close association, the members of the team have developed an almost telepathic unity of attitude. This does not mean that they all think alike (their meetings for discussion demonstrate that this is far from being the case), but that they all seem to be aware of the significant issues in any situation concerning the boys. This has developed with experience, and as a result, on the one hand, the manipulation that was common in the early days no longer takes place and, on the other, the boys find reassurance in the common attitudes of the team.

It is interesting to examine the original concepts and see to what degree they have become a part of the structure.

The staff-training element has not developed as originally conceived. Three borstal housemasters have had valuable experience (as well as making a useful contribution) while acting as temporary wardens, and several members of the staff of Borstal After-Care have had similar experience while standing in for the permanent staff. No planned staff training has been possible, however, but it is envisaged that if further houses are opened such training would be a part of the programme.

A research programme, as distinct from the information continuously provided by the project, is in being, but must continue for several years before it can be of any value.

As the following chapters show, the concept of the group

(experiencing not merely group counselling but highly sophisticated group therapy) under the guidance of an experienced group therapist was sound, its full value being dependent upon the support of a therapeutic team whose members are capable of interpreting and counselling. The thought that the group might become outward-looking has not proved realistic within the context of this project. Whether with this type of boy in this particular situation it could or should is a question that further experience with this or other similar projects may answer.

The projected supporting role of the home has been realized although not always as was originally envisaged. Although on occasion landlords and landladies of boys in lodgings have been seen, the major external support has been given to girl friends or wives, and as relationships have progressed the warden, especially, has found herself acting increasingly as mother confessor, marriage counsellor, and pre- and post-natal adviser. This has proved an important factor, and, coupled with the long-term support the supervisor is clearly willing and able to give both to those in and those who have left the home, has helped to give confidence in the project not only to those immediately concerned but to all the boys and their girls or wives.

The establishment of an outpatients' unit for non-residents has not proved practicable and it was perhaps asking too much of a prototype to expect that it could be. At the same time, the demonstrable value of the group and the therapeutic team may lead to a further experimental project for the non-resident homeless. On the other hand, boys who have left the home have continued to enjoy its support.

It was the original idea that the unit should not be *a hostel* or *a home*, but as far as possible simply *home*, to the residents. It would have been totally unrealistic to have expected the residents to understand or respond to this concept immediately. In fact their initial behaviour indicated beyond doubt how primitive their idea of 'home' was. Simply, 'home' was interpreted as a place where you do as you like, from leaving your shoes in the living-room to staying out all night. Gradually, without externally imposed rules, these attitudes changed. Now, a boy who has left the home can unaffectedly write to say, 'I hope to be coming home next weekend', or can call in with his wife in the evening or for Sunday tea as simply as he would in a real home. Residents bring their girls and friends in for coffee, for instance, as a matter of course. Wedding receptions and twenty-first birthday parties have helped to endorse this content of the project, so that the concept of 'home' and 'family' is more real than might have been deemed possible in what is really an artificial situation.

It has already been said that the previous experiences of the boys included several, sometimes many, rejection experiences. A further factor, therefore, that assumed tremendous, perhaps the most, importance to them, was their immunity, except in well-defined and well-understood circumstances, from further rejection by being turned out of the home. No period is set upon the time they may stay there, so they know that, although they may demonstrate their readiness to leave in a variety of ways, there is no danger that 'they' will arbitrarily turn them out. This allays one of their greatest anxieties and gives them a security they have not known before. This in turn allows them to see that the termination of relationships and the withdrawal of support may be among the normal life-experiences and helps them to absorb and cope with what might previously have been interpreted as rejection.

The distinction not to admit 'visitors' as distinct from 'guests' has been strictly adhered to. This has heightened the boys' consciousness that it is *their* home and, coming as they do from institutions where visitors sometimes assume from the inmates' point of view the proportions of a plague, they value greatly the privacy and anonymity of their present situation.

It would seem then that the factors contributing to such value as the project has may be listed as follows:

1. The group as an integral part of a therapeutic community; the group functioning not in a vacuum but in a situation where its influence can spill over the everyday life of the family.

2. The demonstrable immediate and long-term support of the

therapeutic team and the visible interest of the trustees and committee and the certainty that somebody cares.

3. The immediate and long-term support and reassurance of
the home.

4. Security from the fear of further rejection.

The importance of these factors to the residents is that they are
visible and understandable. One of the boys expressed his feelings
graphically but simply in these terms, 'So what usually happens?
You are discharged and you go to lodgings. What have you got
there? – a bed and a clock. Nobody wants to sit looking at a clock
all night, so what do you do? You go down to the cafe and you
meet some of the lads. And somebody asks you to go screwing,
so what does it matter? There's nobody cares about you, there's
nobody you care about to get hurt, so you go screwing and you're
inside again. But here it's different. Somebody's provided this
place for you, so they must care, and you don't want to upset
them, so you don't go screwing. See?'

The long-term importance of these factors is that because they
do not depend wholly upon any one member of the team,
although they call upon the members of the team for specialized
but not unique skills and qualities, they ensure that the project
can be repeated.

It is too early seriously to discuss the success or otherwise of the
project; it has been running but a short time and the numbers
dealt with are few. Figures comparing reconvictions in the project
group with those in the control groups are given in Chapter XII.
These are perhaps not without significance, but another criterion
is that which could be called psychosocial maturity. It is not
practicable to measure this in relation to the control groups, but
those of us who know the boys and have long experience of
similar boys are satisfied that most of those who have passed
through the house display a relaxed self-confidence, an ability
and willingness to communicate (having had ample opportunity
for both conscious and unconscious communication), and an
ability to cope greater than would be found in similar boys who
had not undergone this particular experience.

This project is merely a prototype, a camp from which the next stage of the journey may be surveyed. Although it has clearly been of benefit to most of the boys concerned, it has, nonetheless, been a learning exercise – not unmarred by our own mistakes – to those of us concerned with its development. Bernard Shaw once observed, 'It is terribly easy to shake a man's faith in himself.' It is even more easy to shake a child's faith in himself and at the same time destroy his faith in everybody else. Rebuilding that faith is as difficult a task as may be imagined. The process of learning how to do this is the theme of this book.

FRANK FOSTER

CHAPTER I

The Background of the Project

AIMS

IN WESTERN society an individual is potentially capable of leading an independent economic and social existence in late adolescence, between seventeen and twenty years of age. This period consequently provides a nodal point at which rehabilitative efforts might be expected to produce optimum results. The present volume reports on the first two and a half years of operation of a project designed to keep as successful members of society severely institutionalized late adolescent boys, discharged from the borstal system, who would otherwise have had a high statistical chance of being reconvicted and returned to institutional care.

The aim was to set up a small community, Northways, which at any one time could house a maximum of twelve such boys. The goal was to elucidate the necessary techniques which would make it possible for these individuals to become productive and independent members of the community at large. A subsidiary goal was to study their social performance in a living situation. If recidivism did occur, significant aetiological conclusions might be deduced; if less recidivism occurred than in a control group, it would suggest that projects of this kind are of value not only with respect to rehabilitation after institutionalization, but also as an ancillary mode of treatment for certain types of individual who break the law and come under the auspices of the penal system. We also envisaged that we might create a model for all 'hostel' situations for whatever age-group, particularly if we could deduce general principles which were, on the one hand, practical and realistic and, on the other, modifiable for specific types of individual differing in age and character structure from the group we were to study.

Our aim was to create a particular social organism as the matrix within which these delinquent, deprived, immature, institutionalized late adolescents might begin to develop and create a new life. Thus they would be the centre of the project and the prime concern would have to be to meet their needs as they presented themselves. Inevitably we would learn as we progressed, but we initiated the project with certain theoretical considerations in mind.

Since all the boys who came to live in the community had a history of delinquent behaviour, it seemed reasonable to consider the general aetiology of such behaviour and, on this basis, to decide in what way we might hope to repair existing damage to the personality of the individuals who would be involved.

AETIOLOGY OF DELINQUENCY

Delinquent behaviour may be considered to have three main aetiological roots, which may exist together or separately in any given individual and may be related to each other. These appear to provide a basis for a diagnostic classification of delinquents which could make treatment attempts more rational, successful, and economical.

1. Situational Delinquency is a type of delinquent behaviour having as its major determinant factors in the environment. In Western society, among high delinquency sub-cultures in the larger cities, delinquent behaviour conforms to the mores of the social system, just as in certain tribes in India antisocial behaviour is accepted as a way of life. Another important environmental factor results from a state of conflict in society when the older values are no longer wholly accepted: a situation typified by a developing country that is undergoing rapid social change.

Another phenomenon is 'group contagion', when numbers of people are impelled by situational pressures to act in an acute fashion that society at large considers antisocial; for instance a riot arising from a demonstration in Trafalgar Square. When this type of delinquency occurs society properly demonstrates its disapproval by a variety of punitive techniques, and no special individual treatment facilities are necessary.

A sub-division of Situational Delinquency is 'sub-cultural'. Individuals brought up in a delinquent sub-culture may have to be isolated from the larger environment until they are rehabilitated to accept its moral code. Whether a sub-culture is labelled 'delinquent' depends on the attitude of the larger group; thus 'capitalists' are so perceived by 'communist' states. Such delinquents may, in addition, be perceived as psychologically disturbed, by either their own or the larger group:

> The nineteen-year-old daughter of a gangster in the United States in the early nineteen-fifties was given a gift by her father for successfully lying to a congressional committee about his whereabouts. He referred her to a psychiatrist because she lied in an inveterate manner to him and her whole family, and was highly promiscuous.

2. *Intra-familial Delinquency* occurs when a significant determinant of individual antisocial behaviour is conflict within the family. Its appearance depends on the balance between the psychosocial resilience of the individual and the emotional pressure that is experienced. Thus the adolescent may be unconsciously provoked to antisocial behaviour by his parents to satisfy their unconscious needs.

A boy was referred to a psychiatric hospital in the United States because he had destroyed a new housing development with a bulldozer. In relating the event with evident satisfaction, the father described how he, as a boy, used to enjoy putting a sleeper across a railway line to see if a train would crash.

3

Alternatively, the structural conflicts of the family may be such that the individual is unable to contain the aggressive impulses aroused in him, which are then spilled out onto the larger community. In such cases help for the antisocial individual is unlikely to be successful unless the position of the delinquent in the family conflict is resolved. Resolution may be achieved by assisting the family; but, if sufficient emotional independence from the family can be achieved, as is likely with late adolescents, this is unnecessary.

3. Personality Delinquency should be diagnosed when an individual, by reason of his personality structure, attempts to relieve the psychic tension produced by conscious and unconscious conflicts by acting out his anxiety and rage on the society in which he lives. In such a human being, ego functioning or degree of personality strength may be so poor that the pain of frustration and anxiety cannot be tolerated. Impulse release and gratification are then sought irrespective of the pain inflicted on others. This can occur in people who suffer from mental deficiency, psychosis, character disorder, or neurotic illness. In all these syndromes the demands of reality are greater than the personality can tolerate. These are relatively fixed personality problems which require treatment before the propensity to antisocial behaviour can be resolved.

Another type of personality delinquency may be more transient. Typically this happens if organic change in the brain is caused by toxic substances of various sorts, or intercurrent physical illness, or, on occasion, merely by problems of growth. For example, in puberty the adolescent personality may not be sufficiently mature to deal with the physiological upsurge of aggressive and sexual impulses, which spill over into the community in an antisocial way.

A type of transient personality delinquency is that due to emotional trauma, of which a typical example is the response of the pre-pubertal child or early adolescent to parental death. Normal mourning helps a human being to resolve the feelings of grief, anger, and loss precipitated by the death of a parent who is inevitably regarded with mixed feelings. If it is not possible,

4

owing to either the age or the social position of a child, the anger at the loss may appear in antisocial behaviour, and the request for punishment implicit in this may be an attempt to expiate guilt. All too often in adolescents, when delinquency appears in this way, it is seen as being due to the absence of parental control; in fact, the aetiology is more complex.

A fifteen-year-old boy in an approved school had reacted to his father's death, which had occurred when the boy was twelve, by spending his time at the dockside of an East Coast port watching the trawlers leave. His father had been a fisherman. As his mother was short of funds she moved with her family to an inland town to be near her relatives. The boy became increasingly delinquent and in rapid succession ran the gamut of being bound over, put on probation, sent to an attendance centre and finally to the approved school.

In an initial interview with a psychiatrist he told him that his ambition was to be a fisherman; the doctor's reply was 'Like father.' The boy's eyes filled with tears. The comment was then made that he 'still missed his dad'. He told the psychiatrist that he often thought of his father and this always made him sad and envious of boys not in his position. He also talked of not having been a good enough son. It was concluded that his delinquent behaviour was part of his mourning process. The treatment recommended for him in the approved school was that he should in the first instance be given work that was hard, menial, and non-gratifying, to give him an opportunity to expiate his guilt. In addition, the staff of the school were to talk to the boy, whenever the opportunity arose, about his father. The boy has not been reconvicted.

Just as some juvenile courts tend to be preoccupied with an attempt to reinforce the conscience of the delinquent, so there has been a tendency for investigating and treating agencies to regard as the most important aetiological root of delinquency the one that fits the orientation of that agency. Analytically orientated psychiatrists tend to see intra-psychic factors as being of prime significance;

those with an 'organic' orientation look for organicity; sociologists seek sub-cultural pressures and conflicts; social workers view family structure. An overall diagnostic assessment considering all the aetiological factors tends not to be made, and therapeutic efforts may therefore be inadequately applied.

INSTITUTIONALIZATION

A particular additional problem that may complicate the diagnostic and therapeutic picture occurs when an individual has been 'institutionalized', which tends to produce what has been called an 'emotional deficiency disease'.[1] It is quite certain that one of the tragedies that may follow on the breakdown of a family unit, whether by death, divorce, or separation, is the production of a number of highly disturbed children. Often they become the innocent victims of a social system, which may make an intuitive attempt to be helpful but fail to use specific psychological knowledge.

A typical example of this situation is seen in children who have to be removed at an early age from their immediate home environment and placed in a foster-home. Those children who appear to take the trauma of separation 'quietly' are likely to find a permanent base, but some react with disturbed behaviour which, to the adult, appears intolerably 'naughty', 'bad', or difficult. On such occasions those foster-parents who do not get adequate support from child-care workers may find themselves unable to cope, and the child is returned to a children's home. All too often homes are run on tight budgets by house parents who are intimidated by their supervising committees. The children may be encouraged to adapt and conform, 'to behave themselves', with little attempt made to understand that their disturbed behaviour is partially the result of unresolved conflicts initiated by broken mothering and fathering relationships.

After settling down in the children's home, the child may then be shifted to another foster-family or perhaps be moved to a

[1] Bettelheim, B. & Sylvester, E. *Amer. J. Orthopsychiat.*, **18**, 191–206, 1948.

different type of environment. Once again he may react to the broken relationship by disturbed behaviour, and the whole cycle is repeated. Ultimately such children may be deemed 'maladjusted' and placed in a special school, and by the age of ten they have become adapted to being in institutions. Society, on its part, continues to repeat the cycle of broken relationships by moving the boy or girl to new environments, principally on the basis of age and educational status.

A highly disturbed personality with a distorted capacity for giving and receiving affection and with a tenuous control of aggressive impulses may thus be created. Such a child is often unable to make an adjustment in the community at large and reacts to attempts at such placements with overt clinging or disturbed or antisocial behaviour. Many such children become delinquent and progress from children's homes to schools for maladjusted children, to approved schools, to borstals, and ultimately to prisons. They may then become long-term inhabitants of penal establishments.

If, as an infant, the child is referred for specific psychological help, all too often it is either unavailable or inadequate in scope. On the other hand, if at puberty, after being placed in an institution, he is seen by psychiatrists, his gross personality deficiencies are often considered untreatable, and recommendations for care may include such statements as 'Needs a relationship with mature adults of both sexes'.[2] The staffs of institutions rarely have sufficient specific training in psychological understanding and, in any case, have so many children in their care that the recommendation becomes unhelpful.

By the time adolescence is reached, if care in the community is attempted, such children are often not accessible to formal psychotherapeutic techniques. There are several reasons for this. The adolescent may not be motivated for help, or may resent the circumstances in which it is offered – often, in early adolescence, a child guidance clinic. Drugs are rarely of value in helping the

[2] This is a typical statement made on psychiatric reports as part of a recommendation from a classifying school to a receiving approved school.

disturbed adolescent, and specialized facilities such as schools for maladjusted children and psychiatric hospitals for severely disturbed adolescents are almost unobtainable for the fifteen to eighteen age-group.

Society, unable to be helpful, may avoid feelings of guilt by projecting its anger onto these children and labelling them 'psychopathic' or 'inadequate', terms which are often expressions either of contempt or despair. If by any chance assistance is actively sought, there are few resources for treatment. It is not unusual, for example, for an adolescent who is a potential murderer or severely sexually perverted to seek psychological assistance and be unable to find it. Thus inevitably the care and treatment of this group of deprived institutionalized people tends to fall upon the penal system. When they are discharged they are of great concern to those involved with after-care from approved schools, borstals, and prisons, who may flounder desperately in their attempts to be helpful. The magnitude of the problem is shown by statistics culled from After-Care reports. For example, in the first nine months of 1962, of 2,992 boys admitted to borstal for the first time, 733 had previously been in an approved school once, 201 twice, and 46 three times.[3] In the four-year period from 1953 to 1957 no less than 52·49% of those discharged from borstals, had been reconvicted; nearly half of these (45·9%) had previously been in approved schools, and 12·8% were homeless.[4] A study of the records of the Borstal Division of the Central After-Care Association[5] clearly shows that four and a half years in any type of institution carries with it a bad rehabilitative prognosis.[6]

Attempts have been made to reverse the effects of institutionalization. For example, during the decade 1950–1960, a voluminous literature[7] has appeared on the rehabilitation of long-institutionalized psychotic patients in mental hospitals, where 'sentences' are

[3] Personal communication from the Director of the Borstal Division of the Central After-Care Association.
[4] Annual Report of the Council of the Central After-Care Association, London: H.M.S.O., 1957.
[5] Abbreviated normally to Borstal After-Care.
[6] Hood, Roger. Personal communication.
[7] Clark, D. H. *Brit. J. Psychiat.*, **109**, 178–201, 1963.

in fact indeterminate. An effort is now being made, with tenuous resources, to avoid the production of institutionalization, in particular by the use of community care hostels. As in many other situations, these are being created often with little awareness of what is involved other than care and protection.

There are, however, few reports of techniques for rehabilitating institutionalized and psychologically disturbed young people, perhaps because society has only just begun to recognize this as a problem. As we have inferred, ideally such institutionalization should not occur. Nevertheless, its avoidance would require a degree of psychosocial knowledge and human understanding among child-care workers, foster-home parents, house-parents in longer-stay children's units, and the staff of penal institutions for young people that does not at present universally exist.

THE PROJECT

The project was, then, devised with all these factors in mind. During the period under review, twenty-one boys spent some time living in the unit, and sixteen of them eventually left to live in the community at large. The shortest period of time spent living at Northways was seven weeks, the longest twenty-one months, and the mean duration of stay for the boys who had left was thirty-nine weeks.

We envisaged that the house be run primarily by two socio-therapists,[8] a man and woman who might be a married couple. A psychiatrist would be a member of the team and a psychologist was also available for the specific study of the personality of the individual boy. Since we planned to admit only boys who had been in borstal, another member of the treating team would be a supervising officer from Borstal After-Care, who would have legal responsibility for the care of the boys while they lived in Northways and after they had left.

[8] The term 'sociotherapist' is used here instead of 'warden' because the latter in no way conveys the degree of psychosocial sophistication which in our opinion is necessary if such small communities are to be truly therapeutic. The term 'warden' is used from time to time in the text for the sake of convenience, but the word was never used by the boys.

There would be in addition ancillary staff, a cook, and cleaners. Only one of the sociotherapists would be full-time and all other staff would be part-time, because all the boys would normally be working in the community.

If the candidates for Northways suffered from severe character-ological defects, as seemed likely, it was doubtful whether pro-vision could be made for the degree of intensive psychotherapy that might traditionally be considered to be desirable. Thus the psychotherapeutic needs of the boys would have to be met by many modifications of the usual techniques.

THEORETICAL BACKGROUND

All of the first group of boys admitted had spent much of their lives in 'custodial' and often rigid social systems, to which they showed a variety of socio-psychological reactions. In addition individuals with a history of severe early emotional deprivation, brought up in environments that are often inconsistent and rejecting and do not respect the individual's integrity as a person, show typical primitive psychological defence mechanisms. If such individuals became 'delinquent' they are personality delinquents and have poor control of their impulses.

In other words, we can say that the boys' ego structures were weak, and any social system which we created would have to be able to act as an acceptable auxiliary ego for them, otherwise they would not be able to be members of society at large. Theoretically, personal control of one's impulses can be said to be based either upon the basic strength of the personality 'ego controls', or upon one's conscience – consciously – or the 'superego' – unconsciously. It can be hypothesized that a conscience is impossible without a superego. Ego controls require the individual to identify with the socially desirable attributes of the environment in which he lives and the people with whom he has a relationship. It will become clear from a study of the Northways population that they brought to all their human relationships a distorted perception of others based upon their previous experiences. If they were unconsciously, or partially so, to start to behave like the people in their environment whom they perceived as good, or to acquire their characteristics, they had to be able to like them. Thus their feelings of hate, their 'negative transference', had to be understood and resolved in order that they might use their feelings of love, their 'positive transference'. The superego of deprived human beings is likely to be harsh and weak, by which is meant that there is little control but the individual in fact experiences a punitive lack of satisfaction. Although, consciously, the staffs of institutions have no wish to be coercive, clearly, conscience 'superego' controls of a more or less punitive nature tend to be applied with these boys over a period of many years, and it would seem that they are unlikely to be helpful.

Punitive superego controls contain an externally applied threat: 'If you do this, you will have to leave', or 'You will be punished'. Superego controls of a non-punitive nature may be summed up by the phrase, 'If you do this, surely you will get yourself hurt'. When significant figures in the environment are perceived as being rigid and punitive, even when they are not, any request they might make is likely to be seen as a psychologically painful superego pressure, from which escape is necessary. For example:

> It is common in the borstal system for charitable efforts to be made for other deprived human beings, children and old people. This is believed to influence the boys to regard this as a highly desirable form of social activity. With the deprived youths we are describing, their initial attitude was to reject this along with other socially desirable concepts that they felt had been inflicted upon them.

Psychotherapeutic efforts with the boys would thus have to be directed towards helping them to perceive the reality of the world and its inhabitants. There was a need to assist them not to project their own aggressive fantasies on to others – and then react as if people were always to be distrusted because of their unreliability and aggression. If the environment that was created was too permissive, it might create a situation in which the group of boys would be likely to produce a rigid hierarchical system of their own. On the other hand, if rigid lines of acceptable behaviour were laid down by external authority figures, the effect might be merely to reproduce the custodial environment in which the individual feels little responsibility for himself. In addition, the young men who came to Northways might be expected to try to create, consciously or unconsciously, the predictable environment they knew so well – a world in which clear lines were drawn, and reward and punishment were dispensed by powerful authority figures.

The solution we envisaged was that the social system as a whole would develop a new morality that was positive and acceptable in the wider sense. What we had in mind was that the boys should be able to identify both with the personalities of significant staff members and with the 'mores' of the system as a whole. Thus the staff would have to be people whom the boys could admire and respect, so that they might wish, providing their unrealistic perceptions could be understood and thus nullified, to be like them.

A way of dealing with unpleasant behaviour in another person who has control over one's destiny and whose actions can inflict psychological pain is to 'identify' with it. Thus, for example, the victims of concentration camps often became highly aggressive and sadistic in their own behaviour. If we wished the boys to become decent people, this meant that the staff had to be aware of the emotional impact that their actions might have on them. The staff would need to understand, for example, that if one shouts at an individual who feels dependent, 'You should not shout', he is likely to identify with the shouting. Similarly, if corruption is sensed by the boys in identification figures, even through the reaction-formation against it, as for example extreme hyper-morality, this is the quality which is likely to be taken into the personality of the individual. For example:

An early appointment to the staff was fantasied by the boys as a hyper-moralistic man who tended to look upon any type of

12

antisocial behaviour as 'Evil'. He appeared to the boys to become extremely angry with them if they did not fit his model of a human being. He was also felt by them to be quite preoccupied with the concept that they were all highly promiscuous sexually. Thus the boys fantasied that he made a great deal of money out of the trustees by illegal means and that he was a homosexual. This fantasy never appeared with another male sociotherapist who was later appointed, perhaps because he was never felt by the group to be this type of hyper-moralist.

There is abundant evidence that human behaviour is partly conditioned by the social system in which the individual lives, as is apparent from a consideration of different behavioural syndromes as they present themselves in the same personality illness in different mental hospitals in the same cultural setting. There are some psychiatric hospitals, for example, in which disturbed patients never become catatonic and do not tear their clothes. There are others in which this is an acceptable mode of behaviour. What we wished to create, then, was a social system in which consideration for others in the broadest sense was a way of life, and in which antisocial behaviour was 'not done'.

To some extent the fact that there was a closed system representing traditional authority in the background of the boys' experience, might mean that any new social system that was made available to them would have the advantage of providing a positive change, irrespective of the special merits of such a system. We might be in a similar situation to the traditional mental hospital when a new mode of therapy is introduced; its mere newness can provide positive results.[9]

Further, the fact that the boys were on parole from the penal system meant that, although they were to live in an environment that could have no real control over their lives, behind it was a system that had. The boys would be in a not dissimilar situation to

[9] Compare the vastly better reported results obtained from the treatment of patients suffering from chronic schizophrenic reactions in state mental hospitals in the U.S.A., at the introduction of chlorpromazine, with the results obtained with similar patients in private hospitals.

a patient in a hospital properly equipped to deal with character problems; if they could handle freedom with a degree of responsibility, it was available to them; if they could not, specific controls were available.

All disturbed adolescents who become emotionally involved in a dependent relationship with an adult or an institutional system are extremely intolerant of the frustration in separation from what is perceived, with mixed feelings of love and hate, that is ambivalently, as a good external object. This has been noted in psychotherapy and in psychiatric hospitals, and the first months after discharge from any type of penal institution that allows relationships to develop constitute the period of maximum recidivism.[10]

Since all the boys would have a history of separation from significant people in their lives, an experience felt by the individual as a rejection, it was likely that they would test out adults in a new environment to ensure that there would be no recurrence. Much of this testing would be done by means of provocative and disturbed behaviour. If they had formed any significant relationships in borstal, since it was unlikely that the process of separation would be worked through in a therapeutic sense, they might act in such a way as to make their return inevitable. If we were able to help them not to do this, we could expect that the wish would be verbalized and not acted upon. In fact, the boys were able to put into words their wish to return to the 'safety' of borstal and they were able to say on occasion that they preferred a system in which one was told exactly what to do and when to do it.

We envisaged that the boys would be able to stay for an indeterminate period, which would be based on their need for the specific therapeutic environment. In addition, when a boy left Northways either to live in lodgings or apartments, or to get married, he would always be able to visit, and we expected that

---

[10] In many Western societies in which the stated goal of criminological practice for young people is rehabilitation and not punishment, there is a significant inconsistency. Individuals are given determinate sentences on probation or in institutions; yet at the same time, in the present state of psychological knowledge, it is impossible to predict the duration of a therapeutically significant interpersonal relationship.

some might come back into residence for varying periods of time.

Since, to an extent, the setting was to be based on the model of a home environment, if a boy wanted to return he would be as welcome as he should be in a good home of his own. It was also thought that this might be of assistance in allowing a transitional period before return to the community at large. Further, at times of psychosocial stress, Northways would provide both a haven and a place for therapeutic work, as needed.

When a young man has been in a British borstal institution, he is, on discharge, placed under supervision for a period of two years from the date of his release. He is generally supervised either by a member of the staff of Borstal After-Care, a supervising officer, or by a probation officer. One of the conditions of supervision is that the individual lives in an approved place of residence, but normally there is no stipulation that he must live in a given home. It was not difficult, then, to agree that residence in Northways should not be a condition of licence. Boys could leave whenever they wished and the fact that their new place of residence had to be 'approved' was not a subtle form of restraint, as there was no difficulty in obtaining approval for reasonable accommodation, which was not hard to find. Although the boys knew this, from time to time, when they felt extremely angry or disturbed, the occasional boy might announce that he was leaving immediately. Particularly if he had no real plan he might then be told, usually by his supervising officer, that he could not act in such a way. Since these types of request were always made as part of an acute anxiety situation, this response was felt by the boys, after they had settled down, as a reassurance that they were cared about rather than as a limitation on their freedom of action. Unfortunately, if a boy were unable to handle himself within the structure of society at large or within Northways, we knew that it was likely that he would repeat the circle of broken interpersonal relationships which had so actively contributed towards his emotional instability. On the other hand, if he had to leave Northways because he could not fit in with the group and then moved into lodgings, the staff could maintain a personal relationship with him. For example:

> One of the boys had a history of being unable to make relationships with people. He became quite disturbed when a tenuous friendship with a local girl ended and when a boy with whom he had become somewhat friendly seemed to prefer another boy. He became quite confused and hyper-suspicious, behaving in such a manner in the house that the other boys feared him. His disturbed behaviour was most evident at night, and he gave evidence of his inner turmoil and feelings of disintegration by impulsively setting off the fire alarm. The crisis came when he made an impulsive attack on the boy who he felt had rejected him.

It was decided, particularly because physical violence was not to be tolerated as a way of life in the house, to remove him straight away from the larger group, and he obtained a room nearby. Partly because of their anxiety that the boys would not accept him, partly because they felt intolerably pressured, the resident staff at first told him that they thought it would be better if he did not visit the house. In fact this was an unnecessary suggestion and he was quickly reaccepted by the other boys, with some initial grumbling about his presence, and he was able to continue his relationship with the staff. He also had continued contact with the psychiatrist. He visited the group of boys for a number of months, but ultimately found a pleasant family with which to live. He took up amateur boxing and one year after discharge from borstal he was still making a fairly successful non-institutional adjustment. Signs of disturbance were evident in that he dyed his hair, a measure of his wish for a new identity, and he was unable to establish any satisfactory relationship with girls. Because there was no evidence that he could tolerate stressful situations, we felt that his ultimate prognosis was poor.

Disturbed and antisocial behaviour may be looked upon as a non-verbal method of communication. It may be a testing, as has been said, as to whether one is wanted, it may also be a request for external control. Unfortunately, in our setting it might have to produce a return to the custodial environment and lead to an unsought rejection, but it is only rarely a request to be really rejected. For example:

A boy was recalled to borstal because of his obvious psychological disturbance. He was unwilling to be voluntarily hospitalized and an important reason for the recall was for investigation and treatment in the borstal psychiatric unit. He felt that the psychiatrist was personally responsible for this. He said, quite inaccurately in fact, but accurately as he felt it, 'You promised me I would never be recalled from Northways.' He meant that he did not expect to be again rejected. After his discharge he was able to visit Northways and had a friendly relationship with all of the staff. He was not, however, able to bring himself to speak to the psychiatrist. Thus he projected his inner feelings of worthlessness onto the psychiatrist and, perhaps because of this, he was able to have a positive relationship with others. From having been a young man who was extremely irresponsible with money, he began to save, kept his job, and ultimately married, having saved enough to move into an unfurnished flat.

The wish to have the staff commit themselves to the boys whatever happened, and the anxiety that this was really not so, was similarly demonstrated by another example:

A boy had to appear before the court for an offence of which, in the event, he was found not guilty. Nevertheless he was extremely anxious the night before his court appearance and was afraid that he would in any case be recalled to borstal. He told one of the staff that she had said that he could come back if he was recalled. In fact this had not been said or implied, but clearly the wish–fulfilment fantasy had become a reality to the boy.

With all these general considerations in mind, the creation of a therapeutic setting in Northways can be considered from the following aspects: the selection of boys for the project; the external social environment; the internal environment of the house, the familial equivalent; the personality structures of the boys themselves; and the psychotherapeutic techniques used to try to modify them.

CHAPTER II

The Selection of Boys for the Project

CRITERIA

FROM THE larger group of institutionalized youths under the aegis of Borstal After-Care, we decided to study those boys whom experience shows to have a particularly high statistical chance of recidivism. As has been said, these are homeless, emotionally deprived young people, often with no parents and with a long history of foster-home and institutional placements of various types. The specific selection criteria we used were as follows.

The age of admission was preferably to be between seventeen and twenty, late adolescence. We decided not to admit older boys, since it was the psychiatrist's experience from working in an adolescent unit of a psychiatric hospital that people over twenty, who may seem to be psychologically 'adolescent', fail to improve satisfactorily if the social expectations of the unit are that they should function in the same way as youths of seventeen to nineteen. Further, an admission age of over twenty might mean that if a given individual had a long stay, the age-range of the population might make it difficult for the staff to relate appropriately to the boys. For instance, in our society, a man does not expect, as would an eighteen-year-old, to account for himself if he stays out after midnight. The latter might offer verbal objections but clearly these are no more than this.

A wide age-range could lead to additional complications in the house, because for the same type of unskilled work a man of twenty-one can expect to earn considerably more than a boy of eighteen. In any case we foresaw some difficulties as a result of boys in training posts earning considerably less than those in unskilled labouring jobs.

A further criterion was that the boys should have been institutionalized in a children's home, a hospital, an approved school, a school for maladjusted children, or a borstal, for a minimum period of five years. In fact, although the records were not completely accurate, they show that, of the boys who lived in Northways, the mean age on admission was 19·4 years ± 10 months, and the average period of institutionalization was 9 years, the longest being 15 years.

Since the project was sponsored by Borstal After-Care and a private trust, all the boys, as has been said, would have spent some time in a borstal institution. In the first instance all the boys admitted should have, as the only alternative place to live, lodgings in the community, the usual place of residence after discharge from an institution for these homeless young people. In addition, the boys had to be employable and not so physically or psychologically disabled as to be unable to work. This did not mean that we expected they would necessarily possess technical skills. Many of the boys who came to the unit had a history of gross job instability during such times as they had been living in the community. A least one of them was recommended to go to a Ministry of Labour Rehabilitation Centre because of his difficulties in relating both to his employers and workmates and to specific tasks.

We did not feel it important that the boys should come from the same ethnic or religious grouping or from the same areas of the United Kingdom. We were not concerned about the formal education of any given boy, nor was the presence of a living parent a bar to admission. As the house was located in a large metropolitan centre, we considered whether or not we should eliminate those boys whose roots were already in that city. We decided not to do this, and wondered whether the boys would gravitate back to their old cultural settings. Since all large conurbations consist of many sub-divisions and since mobility across districts is atypical of delinquent groups, we expected that only boys who had actually lived in the area where Northways was located might rejoin their old delinquent sub-groups.

In selecting our group, we felt that it was important to consider social class and functioning intellectual ability. As regards the former, it was unlikely that middle to upper social groupings would fall into our categories. If they did, we felt that the difference between social groups was so great that it might make for endless complications in the house or, alternatively, force a new identity on such an individual. For example, the attitudes towards sexual behaviour among young people from different social strata of our society appear to be quite different. It is not that any one social group is more moral in the accepted sense than another. It is rather that 'working-class' boys tend to be much more openly aggressive to girls. A middle-class girl who is struck by her boyfriend will tend to end the relationship; this does not appear to be so true for the working-class girl. There is also clinical evidence that middle-class boys tend to be more preoccupied with whether or not they will sexually satisfy their girl-friends, and this issue becomes important in their own assessment of the value of their masculinity; this seemingly is less of an issue with the working-class boy.[1]

In addition, a middle-class boy is likely to be more formally mannered and is much more likely to be prepared to assist in household chores. Finally, since the therapeutic staff were likely to belong to the middle range of the social system, it was probable that they would relate differently to those from middle-class, as distinct from working-class, social strata. In that they would be new to the project, we felt that this might add an unnecessary complication.

Where intellectual ability is concerned, many interpersonal difficulties are created if a group of people living together vary widely in intelligence. If, in the same environment, there is a group of individuals with a high level of intellectual functioning and a

[1] The terms 'working class' and 'middle class' are here used somewhat loosely in the sociological sense. The statements made appear to be clinically valid.

similar group with a much lower level, one group may use the other in a deleterious manner, or they may become profoundly bored with each other. This is predictable, since the environmental needs and expectations of such sub-groups are quite different.

Apart from the difficulties which the boys might have with each other, we felt that a wide scatter of intelligence among such a relatively small group might lead to difficulties, because the staff would have to relate very differently to boys of varying intelligence. Further, if by any chance a boy of low intelligence was admitted, the rest of the group being significantly higher, he would be under chronic pressure to perform at a greater capacity than his maximum.

Those young people who would come to Northways would therefore be of average intelligence (functioning levels of I.Q. 90–110 on the Wechsler Adult Intelligence Scale). We recognized, however, that they might have a higher potential, as it is not unreasonable to suppose that the emotional traumata from which they had suffered would affect their level of intellectual performance. We thought it likely that if they all came from this intellectual range their interests would be similar. At the same time, the level was good enough for training at least in semi-skilled occupations.

We felt that the psychological syndromes from which the boys might be suffering were also relevant, from the point of view not so much of giving each boy a diagnostic label, but of helping to understand what might be expected of him. It was our goal to have our community respect and meet the needs of the individual so that, as has been said, his personality might grow in depth and range.

Particularly when the project first started and we were unsure of what to expect, we had the intention of eliminating the most difficult behaviour problems. We knew that the first group to be admitted would inevitably be exceedingly anxious, as they would face the uncertainty of being in a new society as regards both the community at large and their home. This would also be true for the staff, who were all new to the type of situation we envisaged. Thus we expected more disturbed behaviour in the first months of the project than at later stages.

Since it was also important that the public image of Northways, as far as the local community was concerned, should be as unsullied as possible, it was particularly necessary, we felt, to start with as mature a group as possible within the confines of the larger group from which we were selecting. Therefore we did not wish initially to admit boys whose control of their aggressive impulses was extremely tenuous, and we planned not to admit those youths who had a history of overtly destructive violent crimes. We did not expect to adhere to this criterion indefinitely, but in fact it was abandoned without our foreknowledge. The fifth boy to be admitted in the first two months of the project had a history of violent behaviour for which he had not been convicted. He himself did not mention this until he had been in Northways long enough to trust the psychiatrist.

It was our expectation that all the boys would be likely to have a severe identity problem and difficulties in relationship to women. In the first instance we envisaged that boys with a history of overt homosexual behaviour should not be admitted. We did this because, in our setting, some of the rooms were double and we did not wish unwittingly to facilitate this type of regressive behaviour. In addition, the dynamics of this behaviour presuppose particularly severe problems in relationships with women, and we did not envisage that psycho-analytic treatment would be available. Of the twenty-one boys who lived at Northways during the first thirty months of its existence, four had a history of active homosexual behaviour, which they were ultimately able to mention. However, in three cases the behaviour seemed to have, as a determining factor, the rigid social system in which they had lived.[2]

Bearing in mind that in psychologically susceptible individuals

[2] Schools for boys that are rigid and highly conformist (or highly permissive) appear to have more intra-group disturbed behaviour than schools that are able to give adolescents the amount of responsibility they can handle. Typically, bullying, absconding, and homosexual activity are common in the former types of institution.

enuresis may be partially an institutional symptom, we did not wish to create an environment wherein this was socially acceptable behaviour, and the intention was that boys who suffered from this symptom were not to be considered. This negative criterion was not sustained, as one of the early admissions was intermittently enuretic, especially when he was rejected by a current girl-friend.

The environmental background from which the boys would come was one likely to produce severe character problems and, in certain people, madness. We thought that the boys who were, for example, suffering from 'schizophrenic reactions' of various types, might be more difficult to relate to in the initial unstable phase of the project. If, for example, gross confusional or delusional behaviour was a stress response, we were not sure whether we should be able to cope with it. In fact, three of the initial group of boys appeared on first clinical interview to be borderline psychotics. Nevertheless, we decided to take them, and after admission to Northways they did have the occasional psychotic episode. It was possible either that these episodes had not occurred during their borstal stay, perhaps because of the institutional support they received, or, alternatively, that this type of disturbed behaviour had been misdiagnosed or not reported upon. On the other hand, it is not uncommon in penal institutions for the staff to ignore transiently psychotic behaviour because of the near impossibility of placing such patients in hospitals. Nevertheless, at no time during the two and a half year period did we admit boys whose disturbance, as judged by their records of behaviour in borstal, was so great that they needed hospitalization.

TECHNIQUES

The initial selection was performed by Borstal After-Care in the following way. The pre-discharge officer studied the records of boys to be discharged and selected those who fitted the criteria described. The allocation, psychological test, social worker's and housemaster's reports obtained in borstal, together with the

Mannheim-Wilkins assessment,[3] were seen by the Director of the Division. If the boys were considered suitable their records were sent to the psychiatrist. If he agreed that these fitted the criteria on paper, arrangements were made to have the individual seen by him.

Our first thought was the psychiatrist would go to see the boys at their borstals. We envisaged that this would have obvious advantages. Written reports from borstal institutions do not carry the flavour that might be obtained from verbal communication with the boys' housemasters, and we felt that there might be some advantage in the psychiatrist's knowing something of the institutions from direct observation. In that we hoped to report back to the borstal system at large, there might be something to be gained from their staff meeting the psychiatrist informally. Four of the first group of twenty-one boys were in fact seen in this way, but obvious disadvantages emerged to outweigh the possible advantages.

It began to appear that often the boys' institutional adjustment was of little significance in dealing with problems that appeared in Northways, although some comparisons were of interest. For example, one housemaster described an early admission as follows:

'A pretentious young man' who is polite but nervously so, and rather tense. He has been in trouble twice in borstal. On one occasion he was found to be the chief money-lender and refused to be convinced that money-lending was wrong. He defended his position by saying that he was charging no more interest than one would outside. When it was put to him that this might get him into trouble with other boys, he said that he had bought protection. On another occasion he has been verbally and actively defiant about his bricklaying course for about two weeks, and he challenged me to do my worst. He does not make real relationships with anyone, but he is kind and fairly considerate, willing to give a hand, but afraid of being 'put upon'. I think he is self-sufficient.

[3] Mannheim, H. & Wilkins, L. T. *Prediction Methods in Relation to Borstal Training.* London: H.M.S.O., 1955.

In Northways, on the other hand, the main problems he presented were quite different. Whenever he had a girl-friend, he began to get episodes in which, to use his own words, he began to feel 'as if I go potty'. He described depersonalization symptoms, 'as if people are not there' and 'everything seems empty and unpleasant'. During one of these episodes he tried, on one occasion, to throw himself under a bus; on another, he took 150 aspirins. In addition, he was extremely clinging, was unable to take a leadership role in any project (in borstal he had been a leader), and was unable to share relationships.

Since the housemasters were obviously anxious that Northways should take homeless boys, it was difficult to decide whether the report of his institutional adjustment represented an unconscious distortion, or whether, since dependency needs are met in penal institutions, the whole system was so psychologically regressive for any given boy that the disturbed behaviour we saw was psychologically unnecessary for him at that time. A further problem was that although the boys seemed to accept what was said by the psychiatrist, they were so anxious in this situation that what he said was either not heard or not believed; for example:

> Two boys seen at borstal seemed very positive about the idea of coming to Northways. Later they said, 'We didn't believe a word you said – how could we believe anyone in that place?'

Also, the journeys to the borstals were extremely time-consuming for the psychiatrist, and the boys were diffident about co-operating in the psychological tests, once they knew that they had been accepted for Northways. Finally, the immediate stress for the psychiatrist of being in a situation in which a large number of boys were presented as needing Northways when so few could be taken, meant that interviews became over-stressful for the interviewer as well as for the interviewee. With these facts in mind, we decided to arrange for the initial assessment to take place at the Tavistock Clinic. The boys came to London, either on home leave or parole, the evening before, or on the morning of, the day they were to be seen. They were usually first interviewed by their Borstal After-Care supervising officer, who told them how to get to the Clinic and ensured that they had sufficient funds for the day. They were also told, in a very brief way, why they were seeing the psychiatrist. We thought this type of interchange might help the boy to realize that his supervising officer was there to be helpful to him, and there was some advantage in a first contact that the boy might perceive as non-persecuting.

On arrival at the Clinic, each boy was seen in a clinical interview by the psychiatrist for approximately one and a half hours. The ultimate aim of this interview and, in a slightly more formal way, of that conducted by the psychologist, was to assess not only the boy's suitability for the community but also his general clinical state and possible vocational goals. As regards the former, we were particularly interested in a boy's capacity to make relationships with either sex, his tolerance of frustration, his capacity to handle his own aggressive and sexual impulses, and the extent of his need of external controls to deal with them. If controls proved necessary, the devices that he might use to obtain them were of obvious importance. Also significant were any personality assets that he might show, for example, the ability to be constructive and make decisions on his own.

In so far as vocational goals were concerned, the psychologist was particularly interested in whether or not the boy had sufficient intelligence to make his stated goal realistic. We also tried to assess the adequacy of any specific training he might have had previously.

The first goal in the initial interview was to try to establish a meaningful relationship with the boy. If he showed undue anxiety, as manifested in obvious physical tension and various somatic symptoms such as moist, sweaty palms or agitated behaviour, an attempt was made to alleviate it. The interview would start with a discussion of subjects familiar to the boy, and we would then go on to topics that were unknown to him, for example, what Northways was like and why he was being seen at the present time.

A second goal was to define the limits of the psychiatrist's formal authority in Northways to the boy and clarify his role with him. The boy was told that one of the two areas in which the psychiatrist had real authority was in the admission procedure, and the reason was explained. In a small community it was necessary in advance to try to match personalities so that one could reasonably hope they might get along together. He was also told about the specific regulations with which he would be expected to comply if he came to live there: that he should pay his way,[4] attend a house meeting each week, at which all the boys and the psychiatrist would be present, and live 'decently'. The last point was deliberately not defined. It was made clear to him that if he failed to pay his share of the cost of running the house, the trustees, who owned and maintained the property, might ask him to leave. It was explained that a house meeting was necessary to help to try to avoid and resolve some of the unpleasant tensions that might arise in the community. If a boy failed to attend it might be taken by the psychiatrist that this was, in fact, a non-verbal request to move out. He was told that a boy could speak freely at these meetings without fear of the consequences. It was pointed out that residence was quite optional, despite the relationship of Northways with Borstal After-Care.

He was also told that the supervising officer was there to be helpful. If a boy had difficulty in seeing that this was so, interpretative comments might be made. The supervising officer's formal authority in the house was made clear: it was no greater than it would be if the boy lived in his own home. In that situation good parents ask for the help of outside authorities only when their children behave in a grossly antisocial manner. An attempt was made to delineate the area of Borstal After-Care's function in a way that would be comprehensible to the boy. Bearing in mind the boy's possible hyper-suspicious attitudes, it was made clear to him that because he might live in Northways he was not therefore

---

[4] The boys paid from £2 to £4 per week; the lower figure if they were in a low-income training position, the higher figure if they were in a relatively well-paid unskilled job.

more likely to be recalled to borstal than he would be if he lived elsewhere. In many cases, in order to try to make a valid clinical assessment, interpretative comments about the boy's institutional compliance had to be made before anything in the interview situation could be taken in by him, or before he could speak with any freedom.

In addition, the network of confidentiality in the Northways system was conveyed to the boy. In the present situation he was told that the psychiatrist would give the borstal authorities an opinion as to whether or not he was suitable for the project, but nothing of what had been said would be revealed. Similarly, when he got to Northways, the staff would convey a general impression of his external social adaptation to the supervising officer, as a parent might, but the details of his adjustment in the house were not a concern of his officer unless he himself communicated them to him.[5]

The interview with the boy was open-ended, in the sense that he was not asked preconceived questions about himself. Further, we thought this type of interview important in assessing his capacity to establish a relationship and in elucidating whether, in an open-ended situation, if he became anxious, certain techniques in verbal interchange could alleviate this. Towards the end of the interview the boy was told about the psychological tests, and the psychologist's role with him. He already knew that the interview itself was to help to ensure that in the small community of Northways boys would be able to get along with each other; psychological tests would assist in this process and might also help in vocational choice. Finally, because Northways was a new project, the first few boys were told that from the point of helping them and others in a similar situation, it was important to know what sort of personality might be helped by this type of living.

He would then be seen by a psychologist and in the morning given the Wechsler-Bellevue Intelligence and Matrices tests.

[5] The boys certainly did not believe this for a long time. As a result we think that initially they told the supervising officer much more than they otherwise might, feeling that, in any case, he would be told about them by the house staff. Later it was clear that he was felt by them to be worthy of many of their confidences.

After a lunch break he was given the Object Relations Test and a Rorschach.

If the boy was still considered suitable he then spent a weekend, his home leave, or a parole at Northways, so as to get his bearings and be known by the staff and boys already there. The staff at Northways felt that this weekend visit rarely gave them the opportunity to see the boy as an individual. To some extent the fact that he was on a trial visit contributed to this, but on the other hand all the boys who visited in this way related to the staff with a high degree of institutional compliance. They would present as good a façade as they could, so that in actuality the visit gave the boy an opportunity to see the functioning of the house, rather than the reverse. The boys were, almost to a man, enthusiastic about coming to Northways to live and many of them wrote to the staff after they had returned to borstal putting this wish in their letters.

As for the group of boys already installed, they related to the potential newcomers in a highly ambivalent way. They seemed to leave them to their own devices, although usually one boy would take the newcomer out on a Saturday evening. Sometimes there would be boys who had already met him in borstal. If he wished to gamble they would willingly show him the local betting shop. This was not necessarily as aggressive an action as it might seem, because in the culture of borstal it is sometimes necessary for the boy on home leave to return and boast to his friends of the high life he had led over the weekend.

Both the staff and the boys could refuse to accept a boy, but in fact they never did so. The boy could also refuse to come, and the psychiatrist would visit him on the Sunday morning of his week-end stay to discuss the matter with him. On the following day he was interviewed by his supervising officer and there would be a preliminary discussion of job possibilities. He would then return to his borstal and, if this had been a home-leave visit, he would normally be released within the next four months.

The aim was not to have a boy visit Northways unless there was reasonable certainty that he would be acceptable to the community there, as we did not wish to create a situation in which an individual would feel painfully rejected. We recognized that, because of their previous history, some boys might be likely to act in such a way as to make rejection inevitable and so maintain their institutionalized state. Nevertheless, by the time a boy actually visited Northways, the onus for such a rejection should be clearly on him. One boy in fact did not fulfil the conditions of his home leave and did not spend the time at Northways at all. Another boy absconded from his borstal shortly after his return and wrote a letter announcing that he expected to be 'inside' a further year. He did, however, finally come to Northways.

During the two and a half years of the project, of the five boys seen in borstal, one decided not to come and did not visit the house at all. Of the eighteen boys seen at the Tavistock Clinic, one boy failed to come to Northways because he broke the terms of his parole and immediately after his interview at the Clinic left to visit his father who lived in London. (He has since been reconvicted on several occasions.) One boy refused to have any psychological tests, making it clear that he could not tolerate the idea of 'people looking into me'. He was admitted to the project, nevertheless. Another boy failed to return for his second test appointment and he too came to Northways. Neither of these boys has become a recidivist. Several of the boys did not remember to stay in to see the psychiatrist on the Sunday morning. This was taken more as an indication of an inability to follow through with a commitment, which we might expect, rather than as a message that they were unwilling to live in the house. In fact, they would then indicate their wish to stay to the staff or to the supervising officer.

CONTROL GROUPS

It was self-evident that any assessment of the value of the scheme would depend to some extent upon an adequate control group of boys, matched in as many respects as possible with the boys in the house, who would undergo the usual after-care procedure. This would mean that they would live in lodgings, or hostels, or perhaps with families in the first instance, after discharge from borstal. Ultimately they might create their own homes either by marriage or living in flats or rooms. They would be supervised by either a member of the staff of Borstal After-Care or a probation officer. This control group were not to be seen by the interviewing team and their names were not known to the staff of Borstal After-Care. This was possible because we did not pick the controls until the Northways project had been in existence for two years and until the time came for our initial assessment of results. This meant that the supervising officer could not unconsciously provide special care for this group.

Each matched control was to be discharged within six months of the equivalent boy in Northways. The maximum age was to be not over twenty-one. We felt that this age barrier at the upper limit was justified because, as we have said, on clinical grounds the behaviour of a man of twenty-two may be quite different from that of the same individual at nineteen.

The match for intelligence provided some difficulties. The technique of reporting as used by the Borstal Service was our criterion. Unfortunately, not all boys had a record of having been intelligence-tested and, as will be seen in Chapter XI, the comparison between the results of our assessment and those of the borstal system itself did not always tally. With these factors in mind, we eliminated from the control group both boys who appeared to be quite severely retarded mentally and those who appeared to be well above average.

It was self-evident that the duration of institutionalization was a significant matching factor, and the period was set at a minimum of five years. However, we did not wish a greater proportion of the control group than of the Northways group to have been in an approved school. As far as possible we attempted to match this boy for boy, but in any case the overall proportion in both groups of homeless boys was effectively the same.

A further criterion was the number of convictions prior to borstal. To some extent we had to recognize that this was a function of the amount of time a boy might have spent in the community at large, as well as a measure of his psychological and social inadequacy. Some of the boys in Northways had spent an appreciable period of time in the Services and in a sense they had exchanged one type of institutionalization for another. As a counterbalance, we attempted to match the two homeless groups in this respect.

Finally, we had a second control group of boys who matched the homeless groups in all respects except that they had not spent

TABLE I

Factor	Northways (21 Boys)	Homeless Control (29 Boys)	Home Control (29 Boys)
Age on release	19·4 yrs ± 10 months	19·4 yrs ± 11 months	19·4 yrs ± 11 months
Previous convictions	3·7 per boy (81% from 2–5)	3·7 per boy (86% from 2–5)	3·7 per boy (79% from 2–5)
Average period of institutionalization	9·1 years	10·4 years	—
No. in approved school	8 (38%)	14 (48%)	4 (13%)

long periods of time in institutions other than borstal and they all had homes to which they returned. They were generally supervised by the probation service. Boys selected for the control groups were all released initially to a roughly similar type of locality as the Northways boys, over the same period of two and a half years.

Table 1 shows how the samples were matched for factors other than intelligence. When the results came to be assessed the average period of time since discharge from borstal in all three groups was the same, 17·4 months. If the classification system of borstal made it likely that homeless boys would be more likely to go to certain borstals, we might have been able to have a matched boy from each one, but the scatter of borstal institutions compared with the number of boys studied was so great that this was impossible. Since the control groups were being matched from their records, we picked them on the basis that they showed no evidence of psychosis, sexual crimes, and crimes of violence, although we knew from our interview with the Northways boys that the assessment was not necessarily accurate. Thus on paper we were picking the most mature of the homeless and home control groups fitting in with our criteria.

CHAPTER III

The External Social Environment

THE LOCATION OF THE HOUSE

AS WE have suggested, in all large cities there are areas in which delinquent behaviour seems to be almost a necessary condition for social survival. In such areas there are unstable and poor community controls, and mobility for the individual is within the area rather than away from it. Most adolescents are particularly susceptible to the culture of their peer group, and thus it is very difficult for those boys who live in such neighbourhoods and accept antisocial behaviour without any inner conflict about it, who have a defective superego, to abstain from delinquency. It was evident that if we hoped to ensure that our population in Northways was less likely to become overtly delinquent, it would be desirable to place the community in a situation in which the cultural characteristics of the immediate adult and peer-group society would reinforce positive and socially acceptable behaviour.

Inevitably, there would be a delinquent fringe to any society in which the house was situated, but we were seeking an environment in which the local balance was against it. Similarly, we wished to avoid areas in which drug addition was prevalent or where there were known homosexual hangouts. It was also desirable to avoid placing Northways near another hostel for delinquent youth.[1] We realized that our population would probably relate to people with similar emotional problems to their own. We therefore hoped that such people would not be too easily available and would not be so conspicuous in the local

[1] In fact we were not able to do so, and there was a probation hostel for boys and another for girls nearby.

35

society that the Northways group would easily find them. If this was so, we thought that in our work with the boys it would be easier to help them develop emotional ties with more stable and mature adolescents and adults in the local community. For example, the discussion in the house group of socially acceptable behaviour would be meaningless if aggressive antisocial behaviour was the local norm.

The appearance of the house was, we thought, of significance in helping or hindering the boys' relationships in the external world. It was important that it should not look like an institution, and in fact it was to be in a street of fairly large houses, of which some were still occupied by individual families, one was a private hotel, and others were divided into flats.

The residential district was one in which there were members neither of the upper nor of the lower social groups. It was a mixed middle- and working-class neighbourhood with a largely stable population. The area was contiguous with a light industrial district. There were few slum houses in the area, which was well-equipped with parks, recreational spaces, a technical college, and youth clubs. There was some delinquency, and in one youth club there had been a notorious gang fight; this was the exception, rather than the rule.

Given this relatively stable outer social environment, it then became necessary to ensure that the boys who lived in Northways would understand the roles both of leading members of the community at large and of the members of the outside world who were directly concerned with them. The community in its turn would have to be helped, so far as possible, not to focus its own projections on Northways.

COMMUNITY CONTACTS

An example of the difficulties that had to be faced was as follows:

Prior to the opening of the community, a local highly respected civil servant became extremely concerned about the plan to create it in his neighbourhood. The purposes of the project were explained to him, in particular we stressed the safeguards in our selection procedure, and his grave doubts became a guarded expectancy. He was kept in touch with the general progress of the project, and about one year after it started he became instrumental in helping to create an equivalent setting as an adjunct to a senior approved school for delinquent boys.

In order to try to allay local anxiety, leading members of the community were invited to an open house prior to the first boy taking up residence there. Local people met the resident staff and the whole purpose of the project was fully explained, both in a formal lecture and in informal discussion. There was an opportunity to discuss local concerns, and it was through this meeting that the anxieties of various members of the public became evident to the staff, so that, as in the example quoted above, they might be allayed.

In addition, the whole problem of the relationship of the Northways group to the community at large was discussed with the boys, both while they were resident in the house and prior to their arrival. Occasionally some of the boys made themselves generally useful by doing odd jobs such as snow clearing, painting, car-washing, and gardening, for which they were paid, so becoming known to people in the district in a socially acceptable way.

The boys were registered with a group of general practitioners whose surgery was near the house. They were told about the project and understood the aims and were helpful. They were most understanding with the boys, but it would be fair to say that at the beginning of the project they seemed to the staff not to appreciate how likely the boys were to somatize their anxiety and produce physical symptoms with no organic basis. Thus we tended to experience situations in which we felt that the boys were not organically ill but nevertheless got certificates to stay off work. However, we decided that we might be unwise to tell the local doctors of our doubts, since clearly they had the ultimate medical responsibility. We were prepared, if we were asked, to tell the doctors about the psychological and social functioning of any given boy, but in fact they never requested this. Some boys appeared to be able to abuse the medical certificates for a short time, but ultimately this became evident to the local doctors and the practice diminished.

As far as the local hospitals were concerned, we made no particular effort to contact them until the onset of a severe crisis in which they were involved. It became extremely clear that on the three separate occasions on which boys were admitted for severe emotional upsets during the first two years of the project, the hospitals were ill-equipped to cope with the situation. Similarly when a boy was admitted to a local mental hospital after a suicide attempt, he discharged himself against advice after two days and the hospital felt they could not cope with him. It appeared to us that the psychiatric services of the community were not in fact adequate to deal with the type of emotional problem the boys might present. Similarly, we knew that if we wished to go outside the project for psychotherapeutic assistance it would be virtually unobtainable.

DEFINITION OF ROLES

To try to avoid confusion in the boys' minds about the functions of various members of the community, we attempted to help them to understand the role-definition of those people with whom they were specially involved. Thus the local employment officer, at the instigation of the Director of Borstal After-Care and at the invitation of the boys, came to dinner and had a discussion with the whole group about his role in their lives and in the community, and the employment possibilities. So that the boys should understand how to use the local Employment Exchange and the National Assistance Board, it was necessary for the staff to have a close liaison with their officials and be able to act as go-betweens. This ensured that the boys were able to get the help to which they were entitled.

Mention has been made of the fact that all the boys who lived at Northways were attached, under the terms of their parole from borstal, to the same supervising officer. He was of vital importance to the success of the project, because he was an authority figure with real power, something the staff in the house did not have and did not wish to possess. It was his presence that made it possible for the rest of the staff to be relatively permissive as far as formal rules were concerned. The fact that the house staff had no real power helped to create a situation in which the boys were more able to perceive that their feelings about authority were unrealistic. He was a caseworker who could recommend to his chiefs that a given boy be recalled to borstal for failure to carry out the terms of his parole. As we have said he did not have any more formal authority within the house than he would have had within a boy's home. He saw each boy prior to his discharge from borstal and was helpful to him in terms of job placement and obtaining funds before he received his first wage packet. He would also help the boys to obtain working clothes and any tools they might require.

During the first months after parole he was often perceived by the boys, particularly when they were under stress, as a bad object who would recall them with minimal provocation.[2]

It was the practice of the supervising officer to visit the boys at Northways rather than have them travel some distance to see him. Initially, his visits tended to make the boys feel that the staff were agents of Borstal After-Care in the worst sense, and they would be accompanied by flurries of paranoid anxiety among the boys. In fact, it was possible to resolve this issue with the boys, both as individuals and in the house group. If the supervising officer had not visited the house in this way these episodes might not have occurred, but nevertheless they were useful in helping the boys to come to terms with the real world. In other words we did not try to manipulate the environment so that the boys were never in a situation in the house in which anxiety might be provoked.

---

[2] During the period under review one boy, previously mentioned, was recalled to borstal. A specific episode of disturbed behaviour in Northways led to his recall.

E

During the first nine months of the project the staff and trustees were helpful with material support which the boys might need. They might receive pocket money when they were first discharged from borstal, and a loan fund was created to help them with buying clothes. As will be later discussed, this was a mistake. It blurred the issue as to who would be specifically helpful in this way, enhanced the boys' greed for objects, was too manipulative on our part, and allowed them to manipulate. We then decided that only the supervising officer should be responsible for giving material assistance to the boys. We learned that if the staff had to be purveyors of such objects as clothing, unnecessary tensions and jealousies were created. It also made too real the boys' image of the staff as giving and withholding parent figures.

Finally, the supervising officer had an important role in applying pressure to boys if it appeared that a period of unemployment or job changing was the acting-out in society of conflicts felt in their inner world. He could do this by reminding them, if he so wished, that it was a condition of their parole licence that they be employed.

The Director of Borstal After-Care attended the monthly meeting with the trustees, and during the first year of the project visited the house fairly often. He was accurately perceived as having the ultimate authority role in the boys' lives while they were on parole. At the same time he made it clear to them that he was not in charge of Northways. The boys knew that he and his department had been primarily responsible for the creation of the house and they knew of his attitude, which was that of caring for and about many young people with similar problems to their own. They saw him as being the sort of person who would, on the one hand, invite them and their girl-friends to his home for a meal, and to an extent they saw that he used his authority for them rather than against them, as they had expected. On the other hand, they did project onto him from time to time the idea that he was a rigid, authoritarian person, powerful and capricious, who was really interested only in his own welfare. This projection would occur particularly when, in the house group, they were dissatisfied with the psychiatrist and his role with them. Thus the Director would be accused of selfish self-interest when they felt this either about the psychiatrist or about themselves.

In the second year of the project the Director visited the house very much less and ceased to be a significant figure to the boys. He had had a special function for the boys because at times of stress the interest of such an important figure in their lives could be extremely supportive. To some extent, then, his relative withdrawal was a loss. On the other hand, because of his manifold duties, his was an interest that could not possibly be sustained, particularly if the project was to be a model for others of a similar nature. He and his staff spent more time and energy on this group of boys than they did with the control group and, as we shall see, in the first stages of the project, the Northways boys were also given more economic assistance than the control group. We had to recognize that this was inevitable, but it did mean that our comparative results were bound to be contaminated even if they appeared finally to be statistically significant. In addition, the supervising officer often discussed them with the psychiatrist in relation to his own therapeutic role, and he had attended a specific training course at the Tavistock Clinic. These factors did not apply with the control group.

The avenues of communication between the relevant Borstal After-Care staff, the resident staff, and the psychiatrist were important. The psychiatrist, as has been said, did not communicate details about the boys' adjustment and ultimately he had very little direct contact except for a monthly meeting, with the Borstal After-Care staff. To some extent this too represented a loss but, again, considering Northways as a model for other such communities, the time involved in such contact was possibly unrealistic. Nevertheless, if direct communication in this way enabled Borstal After-Care to function more adequately with the boys, as it did, there could clearly be advantages in it. Communications were ultimately mostly mediated by the house staff and, as we shall see, clearly defined roles were finally developed.

The police force was another group important to the boys. The boys felt that, because of their delinquent history, should there be any deviant behaviour in the neighbourhood, it was not improbable that a police car would arrive at the door for the purpose of investigating the situation. This was a view which we also shared. We were concerned about the public image of the project, and Borstal After-Care arranged with the police that they would first contact them if any boy were under suspicion for a crime in the neighbourhood. This was discussed with the boys and helped them to see that authority figures were not the aggressively hostile people they fantasied. The one boy living in Northways who was involved in recidivism during the duration of the project was in fact not 'picked up' at the house; but when a sum of money was stolen from the staff, we appropriately called in the police.

During the course of their stay in Northways, the boys were able to begin to see the police as having a helpful community role. When they first came, they had many stories of having been beaten up in police stations, but it was a milestone in the history of the house when a boy was able to go to the police station to report that his bicycle had been stolen from outside an underground station.

The trustees of the project will be considered at this point, because they played an important role in the boys' lives. To some extent they were also a part of the inner world of Northways, in that they owned the property and provided a substantial portion of the funds for the support of the project. They appeared to the boys as a part of society which was actively interested in their welfare. The group were told of the trustees' support and also of their expectation that the physical plant would be cared for in a reasonable manner. Since the boys knew that the trustees subsidized the running of the house, they were on occasion seen as beneficent figures who would readily meet their reasonable needs, but on other occasions they became people of enormous affluence who were envied and could be cheated, robbed, and despoiled.

Since the boys knew that the trustees were in fact giving a good

deal, both materially and in effort, this posed a particular problem
to them. As a group, the boys easily became envious and found it
difficult to express and feel gratitude. At Christmas-time they
were all given a present by the trustees, and this aroused in one
boy the following response:

> He was a boy who apparently had never been given a personal
> birthday or Christmas present. At his twenty-first birthday he
> was given a party with a handsome cigarette lighter and at
> Christmas he again got a present. He lost the lighter and said of
> the trustees: 'They are not really giving us anything because,
> after all, they are only saving on their income tax.'

The trustees were on the whole fantasy figures. They met the
boys only occasionally; they had an annual Christmas dinner
with them and, as has been said, gave them a Christmas gift;
the trustee who lived nearby would occasionally visit the house
and was particularly helpful to some of the boys who had
left and lived locally, and one who lived out of town once spent
a night at Northways. The trustee group consisted of represent-
atives of the family who provided the funds for the project, the
Director of Borstal After-Care, and a member of the Prison
Department.

They met monthly with the staff most directly involved in the
project (ultimately we included the supervising officer), and
received a general progress report which included details of each
boy's adjustment to the outside world. They thus functioned for
the staff in a general advisory capacity. It was important to the staff
most directly involved to know that the trustees trusted their
judgement and did not directly interfere in the therapeutic
relationship with the boys. Their attitude was best summed up
in the phrase 'how can we be helpful?' They provided the staff
with the opportunity of discussing on-going problems with an
interested non-technical group who were broadly and helpfully
humanistic.

Since it was an expectation that all the boys who lived in
Northways would be employed, it was clear that employers

occupied a most significant role for the boys. We had to decide whether or not the staff should attempt to set up a special relationship with them. Borstal After-Care staff have always had such a relationship with some employers, for example:

> The supervising officer was able to arrange for a boy with special skill in that field to obtain a job through a contact of his in the television industry. The position as a trainee was arranged, but the boy became involved in a series of delinquencies and was reconvicted. Because of this special relationship, when the boy was released from borstal again and returned to Northways, he was able to take up the vacancy, a state of affairs which in other situations would have been most unlikely. The same employer was also able to arrange for another boy to obtain a post as a trainee in the catering industry.

When the project started, we did not attempt to set up such a relationship ourselves. This was because we were not sure if it would be necessary and because of other pressures which inevitably accompany any new venture.

Ultimately the male staff member became quite active in contacting employers in certain circumstances. For example, some boys had great difficulties in making relationships with others, and with certain employers it was helpful to mention this. On other occasions boys grossly overrated their capacity to do skilled jobs. We did not know whether this was because they had not heard constructive criticisms of their job abilities in borstal, or whether these criticisms had not been made. In any event much of the training they had previously received did not appear to have prepared them for the mechanization which exists in industry generally. It was important to convey this to prospective employers. Another problem was that boys would accept jobs they were patently unable to handle.

Although we discussed with the boys the gaps in their National Insurance Cards, we did not approach employers on this issue. We felt it important that the boys should face the possibility that this might mean that they had been in an institution for some considerable time in order that they might discover the employers' attitudes to their past records.

One of the problems the boys often showed was bad time-keeping, but we made no attempt to control the employers' realistic response to this or to ask for any special privilege for the boys. Nevertheless, there were times when the boys were genuinely ill and yet were too anxious to contact the employers themselves. When this occurred we would do so for them.

Publicity, both in professional circles and as conveyed by the lay press, is a vital issue in any new rehabilitation project. The former was dealt with by telling interested technical people that if the boys became psychosocial guinea pigs under observation the whole atmosphere of the house would be destroyed. Thus no one was able to visit to look at the project without the invitation of the staff and the boys as a community group. On a rare occasion we did ask the boys to invite someone and explained why we thought it necessary. Actually, as a group, they tended to be over-compliant about such requests, and bearing this in mind we rarely made them. One national newspaper which learned about it agreed not to report on the house when the editor understood that this might damage the project. Unfortunately, at a later date, a local news-paper reported about 'a hostel for ex-borstal boys,' giving its address. By this time the residents were sufficiently secure and they were able to accept fairly philosophically such unfortunate publicity.

Ultimately the boys established many ties with members of the local community: girl-friends and their parents, workmates, and finally boys who had left Northways and set up homes for themselves nearby. Those who lived at a distance came back to visit or to stay, not just because of their relationship with the unit, but also because of local ties. They never established any significant relationships with church groups, and although we did not formally seek one, in the first two and a half years of the project we never had a spontaneous relationship with a local minister.

CHAPTER IV

The Internal Social Environment

PHYSICAL ENVIRONMENT

IT IS logical at this stage to describe some relevant aspects of the community's building. We felt that if the project was to be successful there had to be enough living space for a boy desiring relative privacy to have it. Obviously it is important for human beings who live in a group with their peers to be able to withdraw from time to time. There were three large living-rooms, each of which subserved a variety of functions. One of these could be used for group discussions and was wired for sound-recording (which the boys knew); it also contained a record-player. The second room contained a television set and radio, and the third room had books, a sewing machine, a table and chairs, and a piano.

We had hoped to provide furniture that might be not only typical of a working-class home, but also we wanted it to convey a feeling of warm homeliness to a deprived boy. We wished to avoid an 'institutional' look but we did not want to use poor quality modern-looking furniture. We therefore furnished the house with comfortable overstuffed chairs, rather ponderous sideboards and tables, and floral carpets – a style that would have been fairly typical for the boys if they had been brought up in a normal home environment. The dining-room had oak dining furniture and it was possible for all the boys to eat together as a 'family group' around one table. There was a hatch through to the kitchen which was large, commodious, and up-to-date.

It was our intention for food to be available to the boys at all times and for food stores, such as the pantry and refrigerator, to be as accessible as they might be in a normal family. In fact, it took quite some time to achieve this goal.

In addition, we had a laundry room with an automatic washing machine which was available for the boys to use. Laundry was normally done by one of the cleaners. When the machine was first installed the boys used it like a new toy, and it would be used to wash one shirt with quantities of soap powder. This problem tended to recur as new boys came to the house. Various attempts were made to draw up instructions for its use, but in fact from time to time it went wrong through misuse, and the boys never seemed to be able to handle it appropriately for very long.

The bedrooms were rather small and contained two or three beds each. There was a single room which was used by the boys as a guest room or, on occasion, for a boy who might be ill. The boys had their own drawers but shared wardrobes. The rooms were ultimately decorated by the boys to their own taste and were scattered with pin-up pictures of various types. No attempt was made to stop the boys bringing in their own accessory furniture, in particular reading lamps and radio sets.

The garden was pleasant but not large and contained a large recreation hut which was used for billiards and table-tennis.

In one part of the house was a flat for the use of the resident staff, which had a common entrance with the rest of the house. It included a records office, which was therefore inconspicuous. A telephone was available for the use of the boys – an amenity which was, in a sense, a-cultural, since this is not yet usual in the working-class home. Nevertheless, we felt that it would create difficulties if the staff had a phone which the boys could not use, as this would automatically be destructive of the family model that we had in mind.

In the first year of operation of the project, heating the house posed a particular problem. Some of the trustees held to the culturally accepted image that it was healthy and tough not to provide heat in the bedrooms and to use open fires in the living-rooms. The boys were used to institutions, which are well

47

heated, and, moreover, at times of emotional stress, would turn on portable electric fires at full blast even on warm days. Because of the waste and the fact that the house was somewhat damp, we installed central heating.

FUNCTIONS OF THE STAFF

We attempted to highlight important aspects of the physical environment which would assist the process by which the boys would feel cared about and in addition become members of an acceptable cultural sub-group rather than institutionalized emotional cripples. The larger effort was to be in significant relationships between people, relationships of the staff both to the boys and to one another were of fundamental importance. The staff group (see Chapter I) consisted of two sociotherapists, in traditional terms a warden[1] and an assistant warden; a part-time cook; two cleaners; and a psychiatrist.

The psychiatrist spent some two to four hours each week with the warden and assistant. The goals of this relationship were for the psychiatrist to help the staff in their therapeutic role and to interpret to them, so they could do the same, the hidden meanings which might exist behind the boys' words and actions. He also acted as a support for them, as they did for him, in times of stress.

During the meetings everything was discussed from the individual problems of a boy to the non-gratifying nature of the immediate situation, the minor problems that might be felt between various members of the team, the progress of individuals, and inter-staff and inter-group tensions. In addition, support was given to the warden in her personal difficulties when she felt these impinged on her relationship with the boys. For example, in these meetings, it became clear that the assistant's role was such

[1] We have said that the warden was not known to the boys by this title, neither was Northways described as a hostel. To many delinquent youths these words have implications which differ from those of the community at large. Hostels are seen as rigid punitive institutions which are society's extension of the penal system. Wardens are described as 'people who take your pay packet away'.

that he had to have other part-time work in addition to his position at Northways.

Individuals who work closely with disturbed character problems of the type involved in this study need adequate support from an expert, who both is closely in touch with the work and understands their difficulties. If staff do not get this support, they are likely to leave, to withdraw emotionally and physically, or in turn to project their own difficulties onto the group in their charge. Whether or not this support is possible depends to a certain extent on the type of person chosen to fill these posts and whether the staff like each other. For example:

Some of the first staff appointed had had previous experience in children's homes. Superficially it appeared that they would be able to work with the boys in the way to be described. They had, however, worked for a long time for local authorities and run 'good, quiet' homes, and it was apparent that to work with the failures of a system with which they had such positive involvement represented a severe psychological burden. Ultimately they found it intolerable to work with the boys or the psychiatrist; at first they withdrew emotionally, then they projected a variety of fantasies as to what was wanted onto the psychiatrist and the boys, and finally they resigned. The situation clearly worsened because the withdrawal between them and the psychiatrist tended to be mutual, and inevitably the latter found himself in a position in which he seemed to align himself with the boys against the staff. This situation contributed to individual boys appearing to be more acutely disturbed, and a great deal of effort with them was required to prevent a generalized outbreak of disturbed behaviour in the house.

A major problem in making the first appointments was that we were unable to describe their roles adequately to prospective applicants because we could not forecast exactly what would happen. When the first staff were replaced the task was easier, as there was a clearer picture of their role and the type of person who would be needed to fill it.

A subsequent appointee had long experience working with adolescents in 'hostels' of various types and resented the interference caused by the rigidities of the typical system in which they usually exist. His wife had attended courses in social work and they came to the project with interest and an open-minded excitement about its possibilities. Two to three weeks after taking up the post the warden died suddenly, and thereafter his wife took over. Some few months later a young man who had experience of work with youth in hostels and later in the Probation Service, became the 'assistant warden'.

As well as psychological support from the psychiatrist, these two both needed the opportunity to be involved in other activities not directly concerned with Northways. With this in mind they both attended case conferences at a local psychiatric clinic.[2] The warden from time to time lectured to professional bodies about the project, and the 'assistant warden' spent part of his time working in a sociological research unit.[3] Finally he fulfilled the important task of acting as the liaison between the research aspect of Northways, Borstal After-Care, and the Home Office Research Unit.

In addition, both the staff had ample opportunities to be involved in their own social relationships. This is, we considered, particularly necessary because when staff live in institutions there is always the danger that they themselves may become institutionalized in a manner that is harmful. Thus in their free time the staff were encouraged to get away from the house. It was difficult for them to entertain their friends there as both of them were part of a community of boys and both worked awkward hours. It was particularly helpful that both had families who were geographically accessible.

The warden discussed with the ancillary staff their relationship with the boys and in general supported them in any difficulties both with the boys and personally. An example of the former is as follows:

[2] The Tavistock Clinic.
[3] The Home Office Research Unit.

A boy who, in a passive-aggressive way, was refusing to work attempted to borrow money from the warden. This was refused, so he asked one of the cleaners, who regretted that she too could not do this. She was at the time cleaning the bathroom. The boy went to the lavatory and 'forgot' to flush the toilet just before she was due to go in to clean.

As an example of the latter, the following occurred:

A member of the ancillary staff became quite depressed and gave immediate notice. The warden wrote a letter to him offering him sick pay and saying that he was missed and shortly thereafter he returned to work. This seemed to be helpful to the morale both of the person concerned and of the other staff.

The cook had to bear the brunt of many discontents. When the boys, as a group, became upset or disturbed, they tended either to refuse food completely or, on occasion, to complain bitterly of its quality or quantity. In fact, we ensured that both were excellent, and that there was no valid reason for these complaints. If ever a meal was accidentally spoiled, the boys' automatic tendency was to berate the cook. If they were able to do this they would be as aggressive towards him for his mistake as they perceived others, when they themselves had made an error, as being towards them. This could be understood as projection by the boys of their own difficulties. Sometimes the cleaners tended to over-identify with the boys, particularly because some of them, too, came from problem families who had difficulties with the law. On one occasion, when a boy who had left the house was 'borrowing' food, a cleaner appeared to be making sure the coast was clear to make it possible for him to do so.

The staff relationships were felt to be highly significant, since we hypothesized that, if there were inter-staff tensions, a disturbed reaction would inevitably appear among the boys. The boys as a group showed very little consideration for the ancillary staff and occasionally would try to manipulate them against each other or the warden. On one occasion the boys projected onto these staff their own feelings of deprivation in the following way:

> When the house group first started the boys felt themselves to be extremely deprived. They talked of how the cleaners were not getting enough free time or enough to eat, and that they were being mercilessly bullied by the warden and his wife. The boys were not genuinely expressing concern for the welfare of the staff, they were really being concerned about themselves. This verbal expression of anxiety about the staff's welfare was not translated into constructive action, on the contrary; and the boys agreed with the interpretation that really they were worried about themselves and that their real concern was that they felt that attempts were being made to bully them.

Since the boys often conveyed their hostile and manipulative attitudes to the cleaners, it was clearly necessary for the staff, as well as to the boys, that role definition should be clear.

The warden was in charge of the house and had a clearly recognized administrative role. There was a responsibility to the trustees for seeing that the boys contributed their agreed share of the expenses of the unit. There was also a responsibility for the general care and maintenance of the house, for hiring ancillary staff, for ordering food, and so on.

It was a responsibility, working with the psychiatrist, to provide the internal sociotherapeutic environment that was considered desirable. The warden also had a significant relationship with Borstal After-Care, reporting to them on the general adjustment of the boys.

When the post was occupied by a woman, as finally happened, we did not originally envisage that the role with the boys would be 'maternal', because we thought late adolescents would reject mothering, in that it presupposes a loss of masculine identity and an undue dependency to all but the most disturbed human beings. In fact, it was not unusual for a boy to turn to her as a younger child might to his mother. They told her their anxieties about their relationships with girl-friends, and, so primitive was their reaction, that they had to be actively discouraged from bringing to her their sexual difficulties. This discouragement was given not on the basis of moral sensitivity, but on the thesis that it can be regressive and sexually stimulating for a boy to discuss sex with an older woman.

The warden's role was to do everything in her power to enhance the boys' sense of masculine identity, and she would ask them to help when needed. For example, she might say to some of the boys: 'I am going to bed; would you ask the guests to leave, and lock the front door for me.' This implied that she looked upon them as responsible young men. On the other hand the boys might feel from time to time hypersensitive to being 'ordered about' by a woman, so, if they had made a room particularly untidy, the approach was 'Let us clear up' more often than 'Will you clear up'. When the boys were less primitively narcissistic the latter form could be used, and often there would be a variation with the same boy, depending on his state of stress and ego functioning at the time. It is sometimes believed that giving one boy authority over another is a valid technique for encouraging a sense of masculine responsibility. This we did not believe to be true with boys who were as unstable as our group and authority was never given to one boy over another.

When the boys told the warden about their troubles in their relationships with others in the house, she might say that they ought to discuss them in the house group meeting; or if they wanted to discuss with her internal conflicts, which she felt to be too complex or too emotionally charged, she would encourage them to discuss them with the psychiatrist alone. The boys knew that she would not keep information from the latter, but they also knew that they could rely on this as a confidential circle. She noted when the boys seemed upset and tense; she saw that they ate well; she discouraged them from running into debt, and most important, she was an identification figure for the boys' girl-friends, who were themselves almost always members of a deprived group.

A typical example of her role is as follows:

> A mother called at the house demanding that the warden should lie to her daughter about a boy's presence, in order that her daughter should not meet him. The warden told the woman that her prime responsibility was the welfare of the boy; this meant that she would convey to him the mother's disapproval of the relationship but she would not lie.

If the staff were to be satisfactory models for the boys it is self-evident that a lie would mean that the warden would be seen as being as corrupt as the boy felt himself to be.

In addition, the warden helped to ensure that, within the range of our control, the outer world would be seen as consistent. For example:

> A member of the Borstal After-Care staff phoned to say he would be coming to have dinner with the boys in place of their usual caseworker who was unable to come because of a transport strike. It was explained to him that to dine with the boys in this way without an invitation would not be very helpful, and he was able to accept this.

As a group and as individuals, the boys made many demands on the warden and were constantly testing her interest and her reliability. They appeared to resent her private life and would make many opportunities to see her in her flat. On these occasions she would often have to listen, sympathize, or advise. She was perceived quite differently by different boys. For some, as we have said, she was clearly a mother figure. A boy who had been in a probation hostel apparently felt she was a typical 'depriving' hostel warden; another boy used her as an authority figure, to keep his money and contact employment officers for him. For one boy she was at one time clearly a hated object, and with her he was demanding and aggressive and he constantly lied and cheated her if he could; the same boy on another occasion was coming to her for advice. In other words, part of the warden's role was to help the boys to come to terms with their aggressive feelings towards women.

The assistant warden was appointed some time after the warden took up her post. When he first arrived the boys always approached the warden with their needs and problems and it was not until her vacation that they were able to assign a role to him. He was not more than a decade older than the average boy but, surprisingly, there was little general behavioural evidence that they competed with him, although this did happen with the occasional boy. Nevertheless, they did so in fantasy, and in the group meetings their envious competitiveness became apparent:

> At one time when all the boys were in jobs they complained that 'Mac has an idle life'. They went on to fantasy that he had a sexual relationship with the warden and moralistically they projected their own guilt and anxiety about sexual relationships on to this.

The assistant warden had several specific tasks. In particular, he developed a relationship with employers and the employment exchange officials and he would help the boys in finding jobs. Normally the boys found it difficult to initiate the performance of necessary chores around the house, and he would help them with this. Many boys, particularly when they first came to the house, found it difficult to make a verbal relationship unless it was mediated through specific activities and, here again, his role was to help them.

The boys early on became passive in their relationship to him and relied on him to wake them up in the morning and see them off to work. This was a most important function because if they were woken by a woman, perhaps on account of the fantasies aroused, they clearly became acutely uncomfortable. It would appear that around getting-up time the fundamental emptiness and depression in the boys' lives were most evident. They found it difficult to wake and hard to emerge from their beds. It is true that this is a not uncommon problem, but all the boys experienced it to a degree far beyond what might be normally seen in our

F

society. If they failed to get up, or were not wakened, almost invariably on that day they would absent themselves from their work.

In order to make a relationship with the boys the assistant would also join with them in some of their more passive activities, for example, their excessive television-viewing. At the same time he tried to help to stimulate them intellectually; for example, on a boy's birthday, he might take him to a theatre. He also took them driving in the country. In the first six months of his stay in the house he tried to arrange camping expeditions with them over holiday periods. The conscious decision was made that if they were to do this they would have to contribute time and energy in helping to arrange the trip, and also be prepared to make a financial contribution. In fact they were not easily able to organize themselves to do this and it was over a year before such an expedition took place.

The assistant had a role as a male identification figure for the boys, and his age was a great advantage here, since the boys as a group tended to dismiss the standards of the next generation.

The assistant normally had no authority of an administrative type in the house. This was deliberate as we felt that this would indeed arouse a sibling competitiveness when the warden was present. It was also felt that for boys who were desperately uncertain of their own masculinity, power held by a young male authority figure would arouse most destructive feelings of envy. To some extent he acted as a go-between for the boys when they felt the warden to be unapproachable but, given this, they were also not averse from attempting manipulation. They were unsuccessful because the warden and her assistant had a partnership relationship in which they felt themselves as equal members of the same therapeutic team. The attempted manipulation was most clearly seen when the boys blew off steam to him about a fantasied injustice on the part of the warden. He would never allow himself to take sides against her but would explain the motivation for any action and interpret to them their feelings about it.

There were occasions when a verbal rebuke from a woman

would be intolerable and in such situations the assistant would make the controlling comment. If positive action was required of the boys it would be more likely to be forthcoming if the request came from the warden, often in the form of an appeal, since this helped their masculine status.

Finally, the assistant had an important role as the person who would listen to their problems, and he helped them, as has been said, to verbalize their difficulties instead of acting upon them. The boys were often excessively greedy of his time, and in effect he had to exercise control without making them feel rejected. For example:

> A quiet, depressed boy seemed, when he first came to the house, to be able to establish a relationship only over a game of table-tennis. After many such games the interpretation was made to him that he seemed to want to find out the point at which he would be rejected because the assistant had become fed up with him. Following this his demands to play became less intense but his capacity for verbal communication improved.

The extent to which different boys used the assistant naturally varied. If they were too anxious to seek the answer to a reality problem, he often could provide it. Perhaps as part of the process of identification, boys would want to borrow his clothes, and one boy introduced him to a friend as 'the brains of the house'.

The assistant warden slept in a room which was part of the main house and not part of the warden's flat. This made him easily accessible to the boys, a situation with both advantages and disadvantages. If they needed to talk to him he was easily available; but by being noisy late at night, they could either be subtly aggressive towards him or be asking him to exercise some control over them. If they came to talk to him after he had gone to bed, without objection from him, it could, with such boys, be felt as an unconscious homosexual seduction. For example:

> One boy made a habit of dropping in to talk to the assistant warden when the latter was in bed. He did not realize the

unconscious sexual overtones of this until one evening the boy tried, quite inappropriately, to wrestle with him.

There was normally no other resident staff in the house. After the departure of the first warden and his wife and before the second appointee arrived, for approximately four months, temporary appointments were held by a succession of housemasters from borstals, seconded to the community to help fill the gap. They were assisted by the staff of Borstal After-Care. This was a period of extreme role confusion which will be discussed in a later chapter.

The psychiatrist's role in relationship to the boys was based essentially on a psychotherapeutic model, with the important addition that, if necessary, he was prepared to be helpful in a realistic way. We have already inferred some of the psychiatrist's functions but his role must now be further defined in relationship to the staff, the boys, and the penal system at large.

As regards the staff, the psychiatrist's main relationships were with the warden and her assistant. His contacts with ancillary staff were minimal and consisted chiefly of the occasional brief supportive word. There might have been some advantage in welding the staff of the house into a total unit by having team meetings. We decided not to do so because the warden was perfectly capable of helping the staff in their contacts with boys and it seemed as efficient to have this as one of the topics that might be discussed in the regular meetings between the warden, her assistant, and the psychiatrist. The psychiatrist, with his specialized knowledge of therapeutic relationships, acted as a supervisor in the clinical sense for the work of the warden and her assistant with the boys. He was non-directive with them, and this was a relationship of equal colleagues.

Because clinical medical problems appeared from time to time, especially as the boys tended to produce psychosomatic symptoms, it seemed necessary for this role to be occupied by a psychiatrist rather than a psychologist or caseworker. If the latter had been used, the relationship between the warden and the boys' general practitioner would of necessity have had to be closer. This point is of some significance if our project was to be a model for other such therapeutic communities. To fulfil this role we believe that the 'expert' in the team needed to have a clear understanding of social dynamics, a wide knowledge of psychotherapeutic techniques, both group and individual, and a thorough understanding of psycho-analytic theory and practice, in particular in its application to the problems of character disorder and delinquency.

With the use of this knowledge it was possible to interpret to the staff the probable 'hidden equation' behind the boys' actions and words, and also to suggest to the staff possible therapeutic techniques they might use. For example:

A boy was given a birthday present by the warden which he first of all accepted and then refused and returned. The warden's inclination was to ignore this and keep the present from the boy. The suggestion was made that this might be a message from the boy that he did not feel sufficiently loved and that the rejection might be similar to that of a small boy who felt acutely rejected by something and, in a moment of anger with his parents, turned down a gift from them. We therefore decided that the warden should offer the present to the boy again, saying that she wanted him to accept it. This was done twice and then the boy was told by the assistant warden that he felt sure that the warden really wanted him to have the gift. The boy said, 'I thought when she gave me the present she looked cross and as if she did not want to give it to me.' This was discussed with him and he came back to the warden and was able to accept the gift.

If we hoped to correct the boys' disturbed perceptions about their human relationships, even this seemingly small event carried great significance. This was a boy who was unable to make easy relationships with members of the opposite sex of any age, and clearly the correction of his misperceptions in an emotionally significant way was of importance.

There is no doubt that working in an intense way with disturbed young people is an emotionally exhausting task, and when one is close to the situation it appears that they destroy all attempts to be helpful to them. It was apparent, then, that from time to time the staff would become despondent about their work with the boys. If they had not had a supportive relationship with the psychiatrist we believe that, despite the fact that they both did other things besides working with the boys, they would not have been able to work with the sustained involvement which was necessary if the project was to be successful.

In his first contact with a boy, the psychiatrist put himself in the role of a potentially helpful and understanding other person who was on the boys' side but not against authority. Usually the traditional image of a psychiatrist was discussed with the boy and, particularly, the traditional concept that seeing such a doctor might mean that one was considered 'mad'. It was also indicated that the psychiatrist would be present at the house meetings and that he would be spending time at Northways each weekend, so, in case of need, the boy could talk to someone who was not directly involved in controlling his life.

An essential goal of the psychiatrist's work with the boys was to help them to gain insight into their own behaviour and motivation with the aim of developing greater tolerance and human understanding of other peoples' feelings and faults; in other words, to assist them to become less selfish and egocentric. As he was the only person in the house who quite explicitly had no official relationship with the penal system and whose relationship with the boys could quite properly be confidential, they were able to be more frank with him than with others. In the house meetings he had a role as a group therapist, and interpretations would be made to the group about the specific implications of its members' behaviour in relation to him, as well as to each other and the world outside.

The psychiatrist was not a distant impersonal figure to the boys. He came to their parties, was, on occasion, directly helpful with employment difficulties, and arranged for many of them to have part-time jobs in the neighbourhood. He was always available to come to the house when needed and lived a short distance away. In times of crisis this geographical nearness was a great advantage. For example:

At a time when we were without a permanent warden one of the boys alarmed his friends in the house by telling of his wish to commit suicide. Another boy rang the psychiatrist at midnight and the fact that he was able to be at the house in twenty minutes was of enormous reassurance to the group as a whole, as well as preventing a suicidal attempt.

Finally, the psychiatrist had an important role in relation to the education of the staff of the penal system who had relationships with this age group. He met borstal staff and members of the Probation and Approved School Services and conveyed to them details about the project and discussed with them the therapeutic techniques used in the house and the discharge problems of these boys when they returned to the community. These problems will be reviewed in the following chapters.

CHAPTER V

The Personalities of the Boys

The effects of institutionalization

AETIOLOGY OF INSTITUTIONAL REACTIONS

INSTITUTIONAL REACTIONS produced by living for a long time in rigid and hierarchical social systems must be taken into account in treating delinquent boys. These social systems are not necessarily institutions as such, they may be sub-sections of society. If a group of adolescents living in society at large feel an absence of community interest and support they will, just as in a specific institution, set up their own rigid hierarchical system. This will create the same type of reaction as may be seen in 'custodial' schools, borstals, or hospitals. The more the social system is unlike the larger social environment and the less it meets the emotional needs of its inhabitants, both in providing ego-controls and love, and the longer one is forced to live in it, the more likely is it that these reactions will appear. They are not necessarily directly related to specific internal characterological or psychological disturbance.

It is easy to see that, if an environment is so sociologically aberrant that, for example, as in penal institutions in some countries, a young person is expected to polish a chamber-pot, inevitably it will produce defensive psychological reactions that allow the individual to maintain some feeling of personal integrity. The same is also true if a group of boys living in a new housing development experience group isolation, and sociological and psychological frustration, in a feeling that they are members of a deprived 'out-group'. If such boys enter penal establishments it is likely that these aberrant social responses far from being reversed will be enhanced.

TYPES OF INSTITUTIONAL REACTION

A way of understanding institutional reactions is to consider them as if they formed specific clusters of symptoms. Any such sub-division is artificial in that it implies a non-existent specificity, there is almost always overlap. Nevertheless, these responses can be described, using terms borrowed from clinical psychiatry, as 'paranoid', 'catatonic', 'psychopathic', 'passive-neurotic', and 'depressed'. The most typical reactions we saw among the boys were 'paranoid' and 'psychopathic', but all the others except a 'catatonic' response were also present.

When they suffer from a paranoid reaction, individuals are hypersuspicious and project into the environment their own internal picture of a hostile, depriving world. This is usually perceived as demanding individual conformity, but at the same time it is felt to be inconsistent, hurtful, and rejecting. Human beings who see the outside world in this way deal with their anxiety by identifying with the system as they see it and they themselves act towards others in a similar fashion. Thus, for example, the victims of such a syndrome are themselves often highly prejudiced. We found that the boys admitted to Northways were typically either anti-Negro or anti-Semitic, or both.

In a psychopathic reaction, people have a morality in which the well-being of another tends to be disregarded when this inter-feres with their own immediate gratification. They usually attempt to manipulate their external environment to obtain this. In both paranoid and psychopathic syndromes a façade of superficial conformity is presented to the world, which is perceived as alien. This is designed to ward off the interference of others, neverthe-less all who suffer in this way live in their own private world, often one of extreme loneliness and empty despair in which authority adults are rarely allowed to intrude. There is no expectation of assistance and often no conscious wish for it.

In the 'passive-neurotic' response, the individual appears to surrender himself to fate and fulfils only what he sees as the minimum demands of his environment. Thus whatever the social situation, the appearance is one of satisfaction. A typical example is as follows:

> A nineteen-year-old boy admitted to Northways obtained a job as a painter for which he earned £15 a week. When he lost this job he received National Assistance of £4. 9. od. weekly, which left him with nineteen shillings a week pocket money. He had saved no money on his larger income but despite this he appeared quite content on National Assistance and made no effort of his own volition to get a new job.

In a 'depressed' response, one sees withdrawal, loss of affective involvement, and a general retardation of speech and thought with pervasive feelings of misery and despair. Only one of the boys who came to Northways showed this response and for several weeks he sat quietly alone, talking only in monosyllables.

Although we did not observe the 'catatonic' response, for completeness it should be mentioned here. Catatonia is a well-known symptom picture which is described as belonging to the schizophrenic reactions. In it the human being stands quite rigidly, but from time to time there is an outburst of violently aggressive behaviour. The evidence that this is an institutional reaction occurring in psychologically predisposed people lies in the fact that it is never seen in some mental hospitals and is extremely common in others. Similarly, it occurs in society at large only if the family unit in which the individual lives places him under intolerable stress.

There are advantages in this type of broad categorization, particularly when the goal is to reverse the process with large numbers of psychiatric patients. However, with a small group, who can be intensively studied, institutionalization may be looked on

The Personalities of the Boys: Effects of institutionalization

from two more individual points of view, the one concerned with the way in which it affects a person's behaviour, the other with its impact on his experience of life.

Apart from their broad institutional experience of children's homes, schools for maladjusted children, approved schools, and, in one case, a tuberculosis hospital, the group we studied had also had a most recent experience of having lived in borstal. This meant that we would also see the effects of their having lived in a penal setting, which, although it looks upon treatment as a goal, is often felt as rigid and custodial.

THE EFFECTS OF INSTITUTIONAL LIVING

The boys came out of borstal with an expectation that society at large would be hostile to them because they had been convicted. They expected to be ostracized both economically and socially. They thought that if employers knew they had been 'inside' it would be very difficult to get jobs. The absence of insurance stamps and a tax coding was perceived as a label that was being stuck upon them. They had many fantasies of lying to prospective employers about this: of saying that they had been in hospital or abroad. In fact, with assistance from the whole of the new social environment, the other boys, the staff, and the supervising officer, they did not do this as often as might be expected.

It was unusual for a boy to experience a situation in which he was refused a chance of a job, but the following example is fairly typical of what happened:

A boy obtained his first job and said that his 'cards' would be coming from the labour exchange. After three days he told his supervisor and the firm's cashier, having been repeatedly asked for them, that when they came they would show a large gap because he had been in borstal. He said to them, 'If you like, I'll go now.' To his surprise he was told to keep his record to himself and no more would be said about it. He felt relieved but continued to have the nagging anxiety that if anything was

65

stolen from the firm, inevitably he would be blamed. His anxiety level was enhanced when his workmates, young men of his own age, were discussing a newspaper article on prison after-care. They said they didn't agree with it and ex-prisoners should not be given jobs while there was unemployment.

The boy felt acutely uncomfortable over this issue for a number of months. There was no evidence from his attitude that while in borstal he had been prepared for this type of situation. Despite the fact that he was a victim of prejudice, the boy had exactly the same feelings towards minorities as were being expressed to him; he said of Negroes, 'They come over here, you can't trust them, and they take jobs while there is unemployment'.

Once the boys had lived in society for a time, their insurance cards were filled, and they had made a general adjustment, anxiety about their past was less of a problem.

The boys assumed that if people knew of their borstal connection they would be outcasts. When Northways was first opened the house was named with what they felt was an unduly large sign. They removed this. They felt, accurately, that it was atypical of the neighbourhood; inaccurately, that it looked like a prison sign. The boys seemingly made every effort to ensure that their previous history should not be known, but particularly those who were most anxious about their identity would tell some outside person as part of a need to place themselves in society. Thus, despite the risk of social pillorying, they might tell a workmate about their past, often overlaying this with a great deal of fantasy.

Boys who were determined to hide their background might still unconsciously give away their past history. One possible way of doing this was by the use of institutional language, but they rarely used borstal jargon. Specific words they did use were 'the nick' for prison, 'screw' for prison officer, 'daddy' for gang leader, 'shopping' or 'grassing' for telling tales, and 'peter' for cell. However, when they rolled cigarettes they used minimal amounts of tobacco, and it was clear from the size of the cigarettes they finally produced that they must have been inmates of a social system in which the possession of tobacco was at a premium.

None of the boys had any conscious guilt feelings about the crimes he had committed. Two boys complained that it was the fault of Northways that they had stayed so long in borstal in that they had to wait for a vacancy to live there, and one felt that his committal to borstal was unreasonable. He had been committed to borstal with his first offence, an attempted break-in to a store to obtain food. He was at the time sleeping rough, because he was homeless.

The boys effectively never complained about their treatment in borstal. One boy alleged that he had been beaten up in his cell, naming specific prison officers who, he claimed, were quite notorious throughout the borstal system. He was the most violently aggressive of the boys in Northways. His insistence that he had experienced beatings was a deterrent to his own violence, but he also justified his own aggression by insisting that authority figures were aggressive towards him.

The boys would hold up the prospect of a possible return to borstal to each other when discussing the chance of someone resorting to criminal activity. The impression was gained nevertheless that the deterrent effect of a borstal sentence was relevant only when they were functioning well and not under acute stress. At periods of extreme impulsivity it did not appear to be a factor in helping them to abstain from criminal activity.

Perhaps because of the distance in time from the event, on no occasion during the period of our study did a boy spontaneously mention his experience in court with the magistrate, although this was not true of the police force who arrested them. Particularly when they were first discharged they mentioned their borstal housemasters from time to time. They never made a spontaneously critical remark about them. If a housemaster either sent his regards to them or was seen by them they were invariably very positive about the incident. This was not true of their attitude to borstal officers.

We would hypothesize that a delinquent is likely to become

social in a wider sense if he has good control over his own aggressive feelings. One way of obtaining control is by an emotional understanding of these feelings, and this becomes possible in relationship to another person. Insight, to be meaningful, has to be both intellectual and affective, and a split of feelings makes this impossible. An intellectual understanding that an action is aggressive is not as meaningful as an interpretation at the time when it is happening. For example:

> In one of the house group meetings a boy arrived late and began to brush his coat so that it scattered the psychiatrist with the dust. The interpretation was made at once that the boy was needing to show him that in his opinion he was dirt. The boy was covered with confusion and then went on to say that he hadn't meant to do this. Later in the same meeting the boy bitterly complained about the way the house was being run, and he was able to see how he had angrily blamed the psychiatrist, who, consciously, he had felt was not responsible.

It would appear that if borstal staffs are to fulfil a therapeutic role it is necessary for boys to be able to express anger directly to staff in an individual relationship and also perhaps in group counselling sessions. It is obviously helpful when some staff have been sufficiently well trained in psychology to be able to interpret to them what it might mean.

However the issue of what is 'polite' and 'rude' is one that often preoccupies the staffs of institutions. Certainly, when a man is in charge of a group of boys, antisocial aggressive behaviour from one of them must be controlled because a successful attack on a staff member renders him valueless. The accepted concept appears to be that if an angry impulsive person can be taught to relate with superficial politeness to an authority adult in all situations, the problems of his relationships will be solved. At the same time, in institutions, the boys are able to be aggressive in word and deed to each other and often the staff in their turn mistake aggressiveness for firmness.

There was no evidence that the boys were able to see the borstal staff as real people. This appears to be a result of the relationship techniques that are commonly used in borstals and, in addition, implies that the emotional problems involved in leaving the staff and the institution had not been understood and worked through by the boys.[1]

One might hypothesize that the inability of the boys to identify with the positive aspects of the institutional system was partially a function of the failure to work through the separation process. Although the housemasters were usually seen by the boys as good, this was not true of the attitudes they represented. The boys, because of the institutional process, would tend in face-to-face situations to try to produce the answers that were wanted. For example, if they were asked about some aspects of their borstal experience in the initial interview, they might be very positive in words, giving the impression that they had identified both with the staff of the borstal and with their explicit attitude.

However, further investigation did not bear this out. It would appear that the boys rejected those aspects of a given institution which presumably were most valued by the staff. This applied to a variety of matters, from camping to specific attempts at psychological help. For example:

The two boys who had been in a borstal where everyone was involved in group counselling expressed immediate admiration of this system. For weeks one of these boys sat mute in the house group and said privately to his peers that he had always considered groups useless. The other boy had more absences from the group than any other boy in the house.

The effect of interpretations about this is to reinforce the hypothesis that much of the difficulty was related to a failure to work out their aggressive feelings and their difficulties over separation. When comments were made to both the boys about the disappointment they must have felt at having to leave their group in borstal, and about their feeling that both the group in borstal

---

[1] Discussions with borstal staff made it clear that now in their training course it is being taught that separation is an important psychological process. An effort is made to help staff with psychological techniques by which they can help boys in this.

and the present one were forced on them, they were able to begin to participate in the process in Northways.

Another example which shows how a boy might identify with the worst aspects of his perception of the social system is as follows:

> A boy who had been in a borstal which had a 'leader' system designed to prevent the setting-up of an unofficial 'daddy' system said how excellent it was in his borstal because there were no 'dads'. He attempted to dominate the boys in the house by subtle bullying.

This boy was particularly positive about the governor of his borstal, to whom the 'daddy' system[2] was anathema.

Other specific problems which appeared to relate primarily to the boys' total institutional experience were their vocational adjustment and their attitude towards themselves as people, their identity.

The vocational training they had received in their lives before going to borstal did not appear, with this group, to have taken note of their interests or of the realities of the work situations they would face after they had left institutions. The mechanization of industry had apparently been ignored. Thus a boy trained as a baker knew nothing of machine baking; another boy who had been trained as a cobbler in a well-known children's home had unrealistic fantasies as to his abilities and what he was likely to earn. He knew nothing of modern machine techniques. We suspected that one of the reasons why this occurred could have been the institutionalization of the vocational staff. An attempt is now being made in the borstal system to increase the value of vocational training and have staff so trained that they are able to keep up to date with modern techniques and demands. However, one type of vocational problem was perhaps a function of the selection process in borstal. For example, a boy who was passionately interested in electricity, and fairly able in this area, had spent

---

[2] The system in which one boy becomes the unofficial leader of a group of others and maintains his position by the use of henchmen who use both threats and physical violence.

his borstal career on a farm. The social environment in the borstal system that was felt to be most helpful to him could not offer him the vocational training he needed; limited resources cannot be everywhere at once.

Boys who were vocationally goalless had not had an interest in a vocation stimulated during their total institutional or borstal experience. Boys who had learnt trades which might be useful in society, as, for example, bricklaying, did not appear to understand that they would need a period of job training on release during which they would earn less than they had expected.

The lack of a firm feeling of identity meant that clothing was particularly important to the boys. This was true of the sort of clothes they wished to wear but, with this group there was also a problem of a real current deprivation. Because they were homeless and without resources, they were likely to have been admitted to borstal with no clothes of their own. This is explicable because many of the boys had clearly lived in most unsatisfactory circumstances prior to their committal and many of them had been unable to care for their own possessions. Their discharge problem was then compounded because a low income, which is inevitable if a boy of eighteen is to go into a training job, meant that normally they would not have enough to pay for lodgings and to buy clothing. For those who were to go into manual work the supply of socks, underclothes, shirts, trousers, and shoes with which they were returned to the community, was quite inadequate. Despite recent improvements they were all short of certain necessities such as handkerchiefs and socks and for some odd reason were discharged from borstal with only one pair of pyjamas.[3]

They were issued with a civilian suit, which, though of excellent quality, was not acceptable to a young man of this generation. The boys would tend to express admiration for it on the day they arrived at Northways. It was nevertheless clear that they disliked the suit which was never worn in the style in which it had been received. All efforts on the part of the institutional system to avoid this have been beaten by the rapid changes in adolescent fashions.

[3] The prison department is currently reviewing the discharge issue of clothing.

The boy's attitude was justified, because, in any neighbourhood which in they might mix, the cut of the suit was a social aberration for their peer group. This was almost as true for their hair-cut. Thus their feeling of being isolated and not in contact with their environment was reinforced by their appearance. In fact, they did not wear the clothes if they could avoid it, and the first group of boys who came to the house spent many hours in the hairdressers.

For all male adolescents, appearance clearly enhances or detracts from a sense of masculine identity, but this is particularly the case for the deprived and institutionalized boy. It appeared that the penal system recognized a military type of smartness and active work in the institution as helping in this direction. As a factor in the production of delinquent behaviour is the need to assert one's masculine self to one's peers by the way one looks to others, deprived boys may steal to buy clothing.

We have already delineated the broad classification of institutional reactions, and the boys notably fitted this. Typically, on first acquaintance, they were excessively courteous, almost to the point of being obsequious. This was true for a long time when they had a request to make in a stress situation. On such occasions they might lie, and the more they acted in an antisocial way in the house, the more likely was it that they would become polite to the staff. At the same time they made it clear that they did not trust authority figures and they all had an expectation of being punished. Their distortions were almost always based on their inner fantasy of attack. For example:

> The boys became extremely anxious whenever they lost a job, even though this might be through no fault of their own. Almost invariably, when they first came to Northways, they could not admit that this had happened. They might be seen around the house during the day dressed in their best clothes, but deny that they were not working. Alternatively, they would continue to get up at the same time and appear to go to work. If they did not find a job by the weekend they would

talk of having forgotten to collect their pay-packet. On other occasions they might somatize their anxiety and be unable to get up in the morning because they were 'ill'. Only when, after many occasions, this failed to arouse a punitive response in the warden, the psychiatrist, or supervising officer, were they able to say directly when they had lost a job.

As a group and as individuals, the boys found it difficult to initiate constructive behaviour on their own. For example:

The front garden of the house was not completed when the house was opened. The boys in the group produced elaborate fantasies about how this would be the best-looking garden in the neighbourhood. The fantasies included elaborate paved courts and flower beds. Many of the boys were quite skilled as bricklayers, but after one year the garden was still incomplete. When the boys discussed this, it was clear that the messy garden, half completed and half chaotic, represented their feelings about themselves. They accurately perceived the chaos as something which reflected upon them and talked of how people must feel critical when they saw the state of the garden.

The boys were often extremely anxious about being taken advantage of by each other. Thus when one boy began a task he would easily abandon it if others did not join him. On occasion two new boys who came together would cling together, but usually the boys when first discharged were punitive to each other and would appear to lie unscrupulously and cheat one another. Even in those cases in which there was an apparent symbiotic relationship it was clear that one boy was using the other, and this type of attachment did not last more than a few weeks.

Often the boys would callously steal each other's precious, if small, possessions; they would borrow money and not repay it, and they were only too prepared to use a weaker member as the butt for their own difficulties. Their feeling of being despoiled by

73

the actions of their peers was well demonstrated by the following episode:

> Usually, for a short time after leaving Northways, those boys who had gone into lodgings would return to the house and spend a good deal of time there. They were told that they could make themselves a cup of tea or coffee and have a biscuit whenever they liked, but that if they wanted either to take food out or to stay for a meal they had to ask the warden. In the house group a boy who lived full time at Northways complained, 'I don't see why I should have to pay £4 a week to feed G.' The comment was made that they must feel very frightened of losing what little they had to others, and at the same time the reality of the situation was pointed out to them.

Personal possessions were treated by the boys in a highly ambivalent way. On the one hand they were cherished and their loss was manifested by an acute grief reaction, but within a very short period of time it was as if the object had never belonged to them in the first place. For example:

> A boy came to see the warden in great distress because another boy who had left Northways had 'borrowed' his coat and not returned it. He vowed vengeance; the warden appeased him and told him that she would get the coat back for him. Despite the fact that the second boy made no apparent effort to return the coat, within a day the two of them related to each as if the whole episode had no significance. The warden, however, was seen by the second boy as nagging and demanding because she kept mentioning the coat to him.

At a superficial level this inability to be involved with one's own possessions would appear to be a function of having lived in institutions in which the sense of the personal importance of property is at a minimum.[4] At another level the boys dealt with

[4] A social system, such as a typical penal setting, which does not enhance an individual's feeling of the importance of his own possessions probably cannot hope to have such a person respect the property of others. Similarly, if the system does not respect the individual, since he is likely to identify with its attitudes, he himself is unlikely to respect others.

their anxiety by making the problem someone else's. The boy who borrowed externalized his guilt and perceived himself as being nagged by an outside source, instead of by his own super-ego; the boy who experienced the loss got instead a feeling of being personally cared about. Even when there was no apparent relationship with another person over a theft, the boys did not sustain any sense of loss and rapidly their grief would disappear. It was rather as if a small child had lost a toy.

Most of the boys had difficulties with authority figures and, partly as a result of this, all except one boy had a poor job record. In addition, although the boys seemed able to work under super-vision, once it was slackened they tended to become less effective. They were able to work with others who were in an authority position providing that their already weakened sense of masculine identity was not further threatened. If it was they became aggres-sively unco-operative, resented orders, and would either leave their job or be fired.

Many of the necessary complexities of modern living were not understood by the boys. Although an intensive effort had been made to discuss these with them prior to their discharge, perhaps because they had been so anxious in their pre-release period, they had listened but not heard. Thus they did not understand about income tax, unemployment benefits, the use of public assistance, the health service, and how to register with a doctor. The hire-purchase system was looked upon as an easy way to obtain goods, and interest charges were not understood.

The boys reacted against their institutional experience in other ways. Certainly, it is the intention of the system in borstal that the boys shall be able to get up in the morning early and function effectively. Partly, as we have said, because of inner emotional difficulties, partly perhaps because of a reaction against being forced to behave in a conformist way, the boys were bad timekeepers and would pass the responsibility for their getting up to go to work on to others.[5] They were reluctant

[5] Many penal institutions have no visible clocks, the inmates cannot wear watches and thus they have no personal time responsibility. Pre-release hostels in borstals are changing this.

to accept responsibility for their own care in other ways. If they had a physical illness they ignored the doctor's orders for self-care, they did not spontaneously care for their own teeth, and initially some of them were reluctant to keep clean. Some of them came from borstal with National Health Service glasses. These were so badly styled for a young man that they refused to wear them however myopic they might be. On the other hand, they resented the possibility that they might have to contribute towards obtaining a better-looking pair, so in fact they did nothing.

The boys had not responded to the help offered to them during their institutional experience which would enable them to initiate leisure-time activities on their own. Only the rare boy had a spontaneous hobby, and as a group they had little capacity for constructive enjoyment and largely watched television, or, when they had money, spent their evenings in a local public house, although they did not drink excessively.

Most of the boys had spent a major part of their adolescence in all-male societies in which they rarely had an opportunity to make relationships with women and girls. Apart from the fact that inevitably their disturbed mothering experiences had affected their capacity to make such relationships, the monastic institutional life had clearly not helped. At the most superficial level their ability to talk to a girl or to know how one might be expected to treat her was undeveloped.

It is common for human beings who suffer from characterological disturbances to be unable to make relationships of a deep and lasting nature with members of the opposite sex. The non-institutionalized individual who suffers in this way often has a capacity for superficial elasticity in such relationships. He is able to talk to girls and plan a variety of activities with them. This group were unable to do this and their relationships fell into a highly stereotyped pattern. Almost at once they engaged in some type of superficial sex play and it was not unusual to see a boy spending hours watching television with a girl on his knee. They were rarely seen to be talking to each other. For a few days this was the most important girl in the world, the next week they would have another.

There were two clearly defined situations as regards marriage. Some boys would announce an engagement in two or three days, others would panic at the thought that the girls would immediately wish to marry them. There was universal vagueness as to what was required to set up a home and, when confronted with the realities of such situations, the boys would respond with bland denial.

In conclusion, it was difficult to see how the institutional experience had been helpful to the boys. One concept of 'training' is that people should be taught to behave in certain ways. In fact, the boys had largely identified with the worst parts of the social system in which they had lived, and it did not appear for this group that it had in any way helped them towards emotional maturity.

Nevertheless, it is difficult to know how far the boys' difficulties were a function of having lived in borstals; they had, after all, lived in many other 'custodial' environments, both as part of the larger community and in other institutions.

The institutional reactions we have mentioned are to some extent seen in all delinquent adolescents, institutionalized or not. A delinquent who has been in a remand home for one week is well aware that 'grassing' is forbidden, and many adolescents are hyper-suspicious of taking adults into their confidence. It appears that these reactions had been enhanced by the typical institutional experience of the boys. If our results could change this picture and if the boys spent a shorter period in Northways than in other institutions, this would obviously be significant.

CHAPTER VI

The Personalities of the Boys

The effects of emotional deprivation

EMOTIONAL DEPRIVATION impairs a human being's capacity to make and keep relationships, as has been frequently shown in previous chapters, both explicitly and implicitly. Fundamentally deprived people have an inability to experience love and positive feelings, which may often cause them and others great suffering. They complain of emptiness, loneliness, and a feeling that they do not know who or what they are. The façade that they present to the world does not represent their true self. They adapt to life rather than experience living.

Often their actions and their manipulation of their environment represent a mixture of attempted adaptation to the real world and flight from psychic pain. At the worst such people inflict pain on their environment to avoid feeling pain themselves, at the best they live through the experiences of others; as it were, they live vicariously. The pain from which they wish to escape is one in which others are perceived as tormenting, critical, hurtful, and persecuting. Typically the deprived human being easily shows a primitive rage reaction which is tenuously controlled either by manipulating others to exercise control or by a vicious internal self-criticism from which, from time to time, the individual takes flight. To others, these desperately deprived people appear greedy, envious, and unable to feel and express gratitude. All too often they show the world the angry cold façade which they have experienced and with which they have identified.

In general this represents the emotional situation of the boys when they came to live in Northways. As a group, the boys aroused in others a wish to help them, and yet they were excessively greedy, both for their possessions and for their emotional energies. They were not able to perceive how others might feel. Under stress their emotional reactions were remarkably similar to those which might be expected from a small child. They did not appear to be aware that others might become tired and exhausted, and they reacted with fury and despair when their insatiable needs were not met.

A common human stress reaction is the need to have something in one's mouth. This is evident in thumb-sucking and cigarette-smoking, more pathologically in compulsive eating. There has been much technical discussion in psycho-analytic literature about the significance of milk to the infant, and feeding the fretful baby is a way of appeasing its emotional as well as its physical hunger. As will be discussed more fully in Chapter X, we were astonished to discover that under stress these late adolescents consumed large quantities of milk. This was true of individuals:

A boy was being talked to by the warden about the fact that he had impulsively left his job. In the middle of the conversation he suddenly turned and dashed down the stairs. The warden said, 'Don't run away from me.' His response was, 'I'm just going to get some milk.' He came back with a bottle in each hand from which he proceeded to drink from time to time for the rest of the interview.

It was also true for the group as a whole. The variation in milk-consumption in the house was striking. Prior to a holiday period falling due for the warden, the milk bill rose dramatically. At a time when the boys were under stress of any sort, for example anxiety about unemployment, the same applied. This bore no relation to the time the group were spending in the house; it was not normally, for example, a weekend phenomenon when the boys were in any case more likely to be at home in Northways.

Similarly, when a boy came out of borstal he usually appeared to crave sweet things and would easily consume alone a cake left out for the whole group. He ate as if the food available was the last, and when the house first opened it was not unusual for the next morning's breakfast to be consumed the night before. The initial weight-gain in some of the boys was particularly noteworthy; the more disturbed the boy, the greater it seemed to be.

There were certain striking qualities about the boys' thinking. They were obsessional in thought, finding it difficult to make decisions, and then they would appear to take flight from doubt by sudden impulsive behaviour. They were also obsessional in action, and an aimless to-and-fro wandering was common.

Commonly they used such psychological defence mechanisms as isolation, projection, denial, and splitting. They were not sufficiently mature to have the capacity to feel gratitude and they perpetually envied the well-being and possessions of others. They were highly intolerant of frustration and found it extremely difficult to wait for gratification, either material or emotional.

RELATIONSHIP TO WOMEN

All the boys had suffered from early deprivation of maternal love, thus they found it extremely difficult to trust anyone, but particularly this was a problem with women.

As far as the warden was concerned, there was evidence of their difficulties with the older generation. They were jealous of the attention she paid to others than themselves, and were totally unaware of any need that she might have for a life of her own. Prior to her absence on holiday, they appeared to become deeply anxious, manifesting this in a whole range of disturbed behaviour, job difficulties, rowdiness, and anger with each other. Constantly they sought her attention but at the same time complained that she was controlling, demanding, and attempting to baby them. A graphic demonstration of this formulation is shown by the behaviour of one of the boys before the imminent holiday of the warden:

He was a boy of nineteen who had lived in Northways for six months without a change of job. Shortly after being told she was going away he began to absent himself from work, and the warden's diary read:

16th. 'Not at work today and absolute pest. I told him I hoped he would go to work tomorrow. If he could not I could give him no time because he had not let me do my work today and I must make it up tomorrow. He appeared in a very silly mood. He suggested he would like to work tomorrow on the book-shelves he is making for me. I told him he could not do this and that I wouldn't have him in the flat during his working hours as this only encouraged him to stay off work. He attempted to argue about this and made what on the surface appeared to be an extremely odd peculiar remark – "I suppose you think I stayed off work today because I want to be near you."

17th. 'Not at work again today though he told Mac (the assistant warden) that he would get up and go in. He was in all day rushing about the house and generally he seemed very odd. He deliberately didn't come near my flat until Mac returned about 5.45 p.m. He then followed Mac upstairs to the flat. In the evening he worked feverishly in my kitchen on the bookshelves until I had to stop him and he joined Mac and me for coffee. When the girls looked in to address a few remarks to me before going to bed he was furious and behaved very badly. He interrupted them and said *he* was talking to me. My daughter ticked him off which infuriated him even more. After they had left the room and Mac had also departed, he admitted he was jealous of my daughters and that he deprived them of time they should have been with me. He agreed, after some persuasion, that he should discuss with his supervising officer his difficulties with his job, his days off, and not getting up in the mornings, and consequently still borrowing money at this stage of his stay. He tried to blame the worker for not having helped him in the past over this. I managed to get across to him that this was a two-way relationship, using the analogy that it is no good going to a doctor and then not telling him what is wrong with you. Long talk finished up on a very friendly note so I feel he will go to work tomorrow, but don't doubt will have same sort of thing all over again in future and suggested as much to him. I told him I would always be happy for him to keep in touch with me in the years to come. Obviously he was very comforted by this and said he had been wondering a lot about that lately. His half-controlled aggression towards staff and to a lesser extent boys has been very evident of late.

18th. 'He did go to work and of own volition apologized to my daughter.'

Just before the warden left the boy was shocked that she was going away for a week, saying, inaccurately that she had said it was just a weekend. Another remark was, 'You are coming back, aren't you?'

This type of anxiety with older women was equalled only in their relationships with girls of their own age. Their jealousy could be sadly grotesque in its excess. For example:

One boy insisted that his girl friend come to the house each morning at 7.30 a.m. so that he could take her to work. If she failed to do this he would immediately decide not to go himself and he would rush out of the house to look for her. If he quarrelled with her, which was frequent, he was then unable to let her out of his sight.

Where intimate physical relationships were concerned, the boys had manifold difficulties. They tended to use sexual relationships competitively with each other:

One boy got married and a small reception was held in the house, which was attended by the Director of Borstal After-Care, the supervising officer, the psychiatrist, and a trustee. A boy who refused to attend announced that he was going to marry the girl he had known three days on a specific date six weeks ahead. The reason for this specificity was unclear at first. It later appeared that the new bride had been married on her birthday; he had to plan the same with his girl-friend.

Some of the boys were excessively promiscuous, but others were terrified at the idea of intercourse. With the former it was evident that to make a girl pregnant represented a proof of masculinity.

Violence to their girl-friends, who were almost invariably as immature and dependent as they, was common. It seemed as though they looked upon girls as a narcissistic extension of themselves and not as real people who were individuals in their own right. Whenever a girl visited the house, the boys would openly 'neck' with her in a group and they seemed to have little exhibitionistic anxiety.

They talked of their girls in a derogatory fashion even though they claimed to love them and they appeared to have little concept of considerate behaviour. For example:

One boy took his 'girl-friend' whom he had known two weeks and to whom he was 'engaged', to see his mother and step-father. Within a few minutes he had quarrelled, as usual, with his family, and both were violently ejected. Rather than bring the girl home, which he could have done, he preferred to have them both sit up in an open shelter all night.

The boys who felt unable to have girl-friends spent more time with the warden and were more demanding with the psychiatrist. The boys who were able to have some type of relationship with a girl, particularly when there were some difficulties in the house, would announce at the beginning of a house meeting that they would have to leave early because their girl-friends were waiting.

Our impression that, at the beginning of their stay in Northways, their girl-friends were not easily seen by them as real people, but were projections of a fantasy image of what they felt a girl should be like, seemed equally applicable to all people with whom they came in contact. Usually the girls were perceived as having qualities which made them good, while their families were perceived as 'bad'. This split, which has been mentioned previously, was evident with figures who were seen as having authority, particularly in the first weeks after coming to Northways. Thus if the psychiatrist was good, the warden was bad; if the warden was good, the supervising officer was bad. It took many months before they could relate to the staff as people who could be trusted.

In other words, although they might suffer from institutional paranoia, they could also be paranoid. The degree of paranoid anxiety from which the boys suffered appeared to be a function of the relative strength of their aggressive impulses as against their ability to control their discharge.

RELATIONSHIP TO AGGRESSION

One way of looking at the boys is to consider what they did with their aggressive impulses, in other words, what were their techniques of handling the anger that arose from often the most trivial frustration. In healthier personalities such frustration might have led to mild anxiety, worry, and a constructive attempt at solution. To these boys the frustration was particularly great because of the way it was perceived. If the warden, for example, expressed some concern to them about their jobs, she was trying to despoil them of what little they had because she was only interested in money and collecting the rent. If a girl was five minutes late for an appointment she was never going to come again. An example of this type of misperception is as follows:

> One boy said to another, while mildly boasting of his physical prowess, 'If I were your weight I could beat you at boxing.' The second boy became furious, completely ignored his previous remarks, which were about his plans to marry, and announced that he was at once going to lose two stones to prove that this was not so.

Often their anger was felt to be dangerous both to themselves and others. One boy had such poor control of his aggressive impulses that in a group session he impulsively made a murderous attack on another, only just being restrained. On the other hand, the less the boys acted in an aggressive manner, the more likely were they to suffer from hypochondriacal complaints and minor psychosomatic illnesses.

Many of the boys showed specific psychological syndromes. Three of them were compulsive gamblers. One of these lived in terror of being attacked by bookmakers on whom he had welshed; another had to go on gambling until he had lost every penny he had in his pocket. One boy made three suicidal gestures during the period of the project; and five boys had psychotic episodes.

The impression was often gained that the prime need of the boys was to defend themselves against the emergence into consciousness of primitive feelings of disintegrative rage. Apart from the psychological defences we have already mentioned, to do this they would commonly provoke situations in which they became the injured party who had to be rescued. Alternatively, they would injure others and need to be punished in order to make reparation. In one boy both these mechanisms existed. The following comment was made in the psychiatrist's initial interview report on him:

'I would prognosticate that he will be easily led into trouble but I do not think that he will initiate it. When he feels rejected he cannot cope with his aggressive impulses and will need to act upon them rather than feel them. He will probably do this by acts of theft. I expect he will then get himself caught.

'He has to reassure himself that he is cared about and typically he does this by becoming incompetent with money. In this interview he said he was short of money. He mentioned that he had lost ten shillings of the twenty-five given him by his borstal and I gave him five shillings for lunch. Later he returned the five shillings saying he had found the ten-shilling note.'

The boy was in a situation which was likely to make him tense and anxious. Since he felt, as always, that he had been placed in a position in which he had no choice, this was likely to provoke anger in him. He dealt with this and maintained some feeling of integration by being injured, having for the moment lost his money. When he was being rescued, borrowing five shillings, he became more effective and found it again.

During his stay in Northways this boy became extremely distressed and angry at a time when the holidays of the warden and the psychiatrist overlapped. He shared this acute problem with another boy of about the same age. He demonstrated his anxiety in the group sessions prior to and after the vacation by loose, aggressive, and disruptive homosexual and heterosexual talk. He also began to acquire many small articles of doubtful value, and the psychiatrist suggested to him that perhaps these were stolen. This he denied, but in fact prior to and during the vacation period he engaged in a whole series of housebreaking episodes – with the other boy, we thought. He made no attempt not to be caught, leaving many evidences of his presence, such as fingerprints, although he was quite bright enough to wear gloves.

He was reconvicted and after his return to borstal became quite depressed and wrote many letters to the warden expressing the feeling that he was being justly punished. The period of reinstitutionalization was short. After his return to Northways he needed again and again to assure himself that he was being cared about. He did this by constantly forgetting appointments and having to be reminded of them by the warden. He also lost the various forms that he had to take along for a job application and wanted her to look for them for him. When she did this, he would then lose some more.

For a period of six months he maintained himself in the same job and once again a similar situation arose. The warden and psychiatrist were again about to be away from the house and there was an overlap of their absences. As this became known to the boy some few weeks before, he became fed up with his job and quarrelled with his girl-friend. A determined effort was made to have him remain in his job, and his supervising officer discussed this with him. Interpretations were made to him about his reacting to the proposed absences in the same way as six months previously. Nevertheless, he persisted in his job change and became restless and tense. He avoided the group situation on this occasion. Over one weekend, apparently by chance, the same boy with whom he had previously been involved, reappeared in the house having lost his job for overstaying his holiday by two days.

The two boys shared the common acute problem of feeling rejected and angry and being unable to express these feelings in words. In one evening they committed, according to their story, twelve housebreaking offences and were once again apprehended. Both the boys reacted to their own anger by acting in an anti-social way and getting themselves caught and punished.

If the psychological mechanisms of displacement and projection failed to help a boy to contain his anxiety and anger, he might show perceptual anomalies in an attempt to control the break-through of aggressive impulses. He might then become verbally confused. Should this confusion not help him contain his anxiety and aggression, he might then act in such a way as to call upon external authority figures to control him. When all these devices failed, and they might exist together or separately, an outburst of destructive aggression was possible. This hierarchy of psychological defensive techniques is demonstrated by the story of one boy.

Tony was nineteen and his history was as follows. Because of impossible home conditions he was first placed in a children's home for three years at the age of six as being in need of 'care and protection'. He was then home with his unhappy quarrelsome parents for two years and was next, at the age of eleven, returned to a home as being 'beyond parental control'. Running away from the home, he committed a minor offence, stealing food, and as he was clearly most difficult to handle, he was sent to an approved school.

Thence he went to another training school and when he left at the age of sixteen he had a series of jobs, six in all, in eighteen months. He then spent a short period of time in a detention centre.

H

Finally he was committed to a borstal for 'Taking and driving away a motor vehicle without the owner's consent'.

From the age of eleven he was known to have had in all seven offences, all relatively minor. Rather boastfully, he said to the psychiatrist interviewing him for Northways that he had stolen some £700 worth of money and goods prior to his committal to borstal. The boy's psychological test picture demonstrated his problems as seen in standard situations. The relevant aspects of the report are as follows:

'He showed a verbal I.Q. of 78 but this was demonstrably related to his inadequate verbal education and he was so insecure during tests that he was reluctant to make any sort of guess. His thinking was concrete rather than abstract. Potentially, however, his intelligence was thought to be average; on Raven's Progressive Matrices he scored an I.Q. of 105 and his performance I.Q. was 91.'

The quality of his stories on projective tests also implied that his intelligence was at least potentially average. Their significance was, however, in showing his difficulties both in handling his own aggression and in making relationships with others. The test used was a test of thematic apperception, the Object Relations Test. As far as aggression was concerned, the report read:

'One of the main themes is his attempt to avoid the expression of his unconscious aggressive impulses. On the first few cards he avoided meeting the implied problems by displacing them. With oedipal cards [test cards in which figures are seen in vague outline of a man and woman together with a third figure at a slight distance], this mechanism became less effective. Certain perceptual anomalies then occurred. However, in spite of the perceptual distortion, the aggressive impulses broke through and in the subsequent cards he attempted to deal with them by the evocation of external superego figures, e.g. the police. His aggressive impulses are felt to be death-dealing and are particularly aroused when he is attempting to satisfy his greedy impulses and also when he experiences a sense of rejection. He cannot control these by identifying with a strong father figure as the image of his father is either as a drunken man or a weak and weeping individual. This does not provide a secure internal controlling figure. In fact he experiences a far greater feeling of security in relation to a stern and reliable police force who are seen both as able to control aggressive impulses and as able to make reparative efforts.'

The report on his ability to make relationships is as follows:

Although in fantasy he seeks a relationship with a woman, in fact his sexuality is felt to be so dangerous to her that in his stories a man and woman have to be kept apart. The woman is then felt to withhold herself both in her maternal orally supplying role, and as a sexual object. He never feels he can really rely on women and has a far greater sense of security when he possesses something concrete, for example, money.

The final summary showed this conclusion:

He has a fairly wide range of primitive defences: denial, displacement, and projection. None of these effectively protects him from the anxiety aroused both by his compulsive greed and by his aggressive impulses. Although he attempts to make satisfying human relationships these are generally conceived of in highly exciting terms which again arouse anxiety rather than provide security.

In the clinical interview he alternated between passive compliance and boastfulness of his own abilities, delinquent and otherwise. Interpretations about this did not change his stated attitude, and the impression was gained that there was a rigidity about his need to keep the psychiatrist as a distrusted authority figure. He had arrived for the interview half an hour late, which he ascribed to external factors beyond his control. He made many critical comments about his mother in this interview, but when he arrived at Northways for his weekend he failed to stay in on Sunday morning to discuss whether or not he wanted to live there.

Instead he went to see his mother who lived in another neighbourhood, despite her stated reluctance to be involved with him.

After two weeks in the unit he said in a group meeting 'I am
bored, and it's dangerous when I feel that way'. He continued
to haunt his old home district. He got a job as a butcher and it
was apparent that he obtained a great deal of satisfaction in this.
The impression was gained from watching him work that he
found it exciting. He remarked that 'It's all right providing I
do not have to meet people', and he hinted darkly at the
motives of other employees in the job.

His problems with women were also evident. He rejected any
contact with the warden, saying openly in the group that women
were not to be trusted and referring to her as a 'female screw'. He
stated that he had a girl-friend who lived some ten miles away
but no one knew her name and it seems doubtful whether she
existed.

He hoarded his money to buy a car and finally obtained
one, he said, for ten pounds. He refused to take note of the fact
that in order to bring the car to Northways it would need to be
taxed, insured, and tested for roadworthiness, further that he
himself would require a valid driving licence. When the warden
reminded him of this and refused to arrange to drive it herself,
pointing out that she had no licence anyway, he announced after
some few days' delay, in the middle of a snowstorm, that he was
going to fetch it. He later returned to the house announcing that
the wheels had been stolen, and he proceeded to berate the warden,
saying it was all her fault and women could not be relied upon in
any case.

These events seemed to confirm the inferences that were drawn
from the projective test material. Whether the car was fact or
fantasy, the whole project was undertaken at a time when he was
just discharged from borstal, was anxious and insecure, and thus
likely to feel the need for external control. The car too established
a working relationship with the warden who in fact withheld
from him the immediate gratification that he sought. Similarly

he repeated the situation which was so traumatic for him of feeling a woman to be unreliable.

Whenever he had a request to make or was in a stress situation he appeared to become quite confused, and it was impossible to see any coherence in his remarks. The impression was gained that he was effectively psychotic; the warden commented, 'He seems quite mad.'

Situations which might arouse anger were ones which some of the boys had to avoid. Actions which on the surface might seem inexplicable could sometimes be understood if we were aware of this need. A young man of twenty, a painter and decorator, was in the following situation:

> During the course of one week the impression was gained that he had impulsively left his job, although he denied this. He said that he was not working because of bad weather and the firm was engaged only in outside work. After the group meeting held at the end of the week he asked if he could see the psychiatrist alone, and when another boy made a similar request he told him, 'Don't wait, I shall need several hours.' Apparently he had been off work for two days and as soon as he had returned he had impulsively quit before his boss had time 'to say a word'. This action was consciously based on a fantasy of being severely reprimanded which, after much discussion, he revealed. He was then asked why he was afraid of this and he said, 'It's not him I'm afraid of, it's me,' and he talked of how angry he might feel and what he might do.

The impression was gained during this interview that he was consciously worried about other things too which he persistently denied, although somewhat affectlessly. The next day it became evident that he had in fact cheated the public assistance authority by telling them he had received no money for the previous week when in fact he obtained back pay that was due to him.

It was possible for the psychiatrist to reach this understanding with the boy rapidly because the projective material in the psychological tests had already demonstrated that avoidance was one of his ways of dealing with anger. Since he was diabetic, the psychologist had been asked about the degree of his self-destructiveness. We were concerned that he might use his diabetes to precipitate either hypo- or hyperglycaemic coma in situations which were felt by him to be stressful. In fact the psychologist reported:

'Although he may use his illness in a self-destructive way he is more afraid of his murderous impulses. He avoids situations in which they might appear and seeks external control against them. His main defences are denial, projection, and detachment of feeling. He reveals himself to be a very dependent person who has to steal good things for himself since he does not perceive himself as good enough to be given them.'

In discussing the effects of institutionalization, we have mentioned the boys' insecure feelings of masculine identity and their need to prove that they belonged to the group of young males in our society, by dressing in a typical rather stereotyped way. This is to some extent the problem of all young male adolescents, but it is clear that this group had particular sensitivities about their own body image. They were anxious about physical damage to themselves and were easily hypochondriacal. They did not however care for themselves physically and a high proportion of boys had severely bitten fingernails. They did not have the pride in their own bodies that one might expect from late adolescents. They talked of keeping fit, of going swimming, boxing, and running but on the whole none of these activities was carried through to conclusion.

Their stated fantasies were simple wish-fulfilments, rather as if they were constantly awaiting a fairy godmother who would give them the good things of life. They could not see that effort was required from themselves. They openly lived for the day not, as with some adolescents, because they consciously considered the future as unbearable, but because they were unable to consider it at all. It was as if they had no time-sense. They would wish for holidays and 'Castles in Spain', but spend their immediate substance so as to make their wishes unrealizable.

They seemed to find it difficult to involve themselves in the real world. Thus they were ignorant of day-to-day events. They were, for example, apparently unaffected by the political crisis in Cuba. To put this in more technical terms they seemed unable to cathect the real world except in so far as it provided them with immediate gratification or pain and frustration. Excitement appeared to keep them alive, whether sexually, in a physical sense, or greedily demanding cigarettes, or in their excited envy of the real or fantasied affluence of others. When they were not experiencing this, or the anxiety of being punished for some real or imaginary misdemeanour, they appeared to be emotionally dead.

Their superegos, as we have said, were harsh but weak. Some of them, when feeling deprived and filled with the injustices of their situation, would talk of robbing others with a marked lack of concern which was so bizarre as to be psychotic in quality. One boy said, 'If I don't have money, I'll just have to swindle the public assistance.' Another got himself appointed as an agent for a mail-order house; three boys in the house got watches and immediately sold them. They had no apparent thought for the hire-purchase agreement they had signed or how they were to meet the weekly payments.

The general effect, then, of their emotional deprivation was that the boys were fixated at a primitive stage of emotional development. They were emotional infants. They were greedy as babies, hypersuspicious, withdrawn from the real world, and perpetually anxious about being robbed and despoiled themselves, although all too ready to do the same to others. In short, the absence of love from their lives had made it impossible for them to experience love for others.

Children reveal their anxieties in their play and in the indirection of their remarks. For example, it is not unusual when a child has been ill in a hospital for him to play 'hospitals' and 'operations' for many weeks after discharge. Similarly, if a parent of another child in the neighbourhood dies, weeks later a child may say, 'Only old people die; Daddy, are you old?' Using their own physical selves as playthings, these boys showed similar behaviour.

A boy who was anxious about his sanity would say, 'How do you know when people are mad?', a boy who was concerned about his own sexuality said, 'Don't you think X is queer?' They demonstrated their anxiety about their inner organization by creating physical chaos around themselves. They were not normally destructive, but when a group of them had been in the sitting-room for a time it often began to look excessively dirty and chaotic. They liked to live in extreme heat, which was perhaps a measure of their inner lack of warmth. When watching television they normally sat in the dark and they generally disliked bright lights. Their lies were usually simple and easily spotted.

There was thus a great communality in their emotional development. It now becomes appropriate to consider how their criminal records in the past fitted into this picture, and what were the emotional assets they showed that might lead us to hope that their overall prognosis, as regards both recidivism and their general life adjustment, might be improved.

CHAPTER VII

Assets and Liabilities of the Boys' Personalities

THE CRIMINAL RECORDS OF THE BOYS

THERE WERE many relevant aspects of the boys' life experiences other than the effects of institutionalization and emotional deprivation already mentioned. In particular their record of convictions and the type of crime they had committed were significant in terms both of what we might expect in Northways and of the indications we might get about their personality structure. Inevitably they had committed more crimes than those for which they were caught, but some overall truths could nevertheless be deduced, especially in comparison with the control groups.

The type of crime a boy commits may indicate something of his personality characteristics, even though important determinants of what is actually done are current fashions in the type of crime and subcultural pressures. Crimes of violence, even though they may also be a result of other pressures, as, for example, group contagion, indicate something of a human being's capacity to control his own aggressive impulses and the extent to which he cares about the feelings of others. Similarly, stealing a motor vehicle may be associated with a wish for excitement; pick-pocketing implies certain common personality characteristics;[1] and theft, although it may be associated with a wish to acquire goods with no acceptable social effort, is commonly associated with emotional deprivation. The quality of a crime, particularly in

---

[1] Zilboorg, G. *The Psychology of the Criminal Act and Punishment*, p. 51. London: Hogarth, 1955.

95

terms of how hurtful it is to others, is also of significance. If, for example, the number of reconvictions in the Northways group was no fewer than in the control groups, but if the crimes committed were less aggressive to others, it would be reasonable to deduce that the group had acquired something positive from their experience. In our small samples (twenty-one homeless boys in Northways, twenty-nine not in Northways, and twenty-nine with homes), because of our selection technique, the number of crimes of violence prior to borstal conviction was low and not

TABLE 2   PREVIOUS OFFENCES

Offences	Homeless Institutionalized Boys (50 Boys)	Boys with Homes (29 Boys)
Theft (larceny, breaking and entering)	144 (77%)	70 (65%)
Taking and driving away a motor vehicle	15 (8·0%)	22 (20·0%)
Sexual	3	0
Violent (grievous and actual bodily harm and assault)	5	1
Miscellaneous (including suspected person, loitering, drunk and disorderly, arson, fraud)	20	15
Totals	187	108

significantly different in each group. For example, one boy who came to Northways was known to have had a conviction for assault, another had been involved in such episodes but not convicted for them, and a third had attacked an officer in borstal.

A comparison of the types of crime committed in the three comparative groups (shown in *Table 2*) is revealing. After we had matched for other factors and as we attempted to match for the number of prior convictions, it became apparent that, among the boys who came to Northways, a high proportion of previous convictions was for theft (77·0%), of which thirty-five were for 'larceny' and seventeen for 'breaking and entering'. There were three convictions for sexual offences. Two of these were homosexual, in the same boy; one was for indecent exposure which, from the record, looked like adolescent exhibitionism. In the control group of homeless boys there was effectively the same proportion of crimes for theft (78·0%) and no sexual offences. In the control group of boys who had homes the situation with sexual offences was similar but the proportion of crimes for theft was smaller (65·0%). The figure for sexual crimes is low compared with the 2% figure given for all borstal offences. It may be that this is a function of our selection but, on the other hand, this was the younger age group of the borstal population on conviction. The figures indicate that in this sample there is a trend for more severely deprived youths to be more likely to steal than others who, at any rate, in that they have parents and homes, were less deprived. This might be expected on theoretical grounds in that much of the stealing of small children has as one aetiological basis the feeling that they are unloved.

If one considers 'taking and driving away a vehicle without the owner's consent', a crime which is, as we have said, exciting and stimulating and is often a conscious attempt to escape boredom, 8% of all the crimes committed by homeless boys, and 20·0% of those committed by the boys with homes were for this offence. The difference between the homeless group and the boys with homes is, in this case, statistically significant.

THE INSTITUTIONAL EXPERIENCE OF THE BOYS

Eight of the twenty-one boys who lived in Northways had been to approved schools, fourteen of the twenty-nine homeless non-Northways group, and four of the twenty-nine boys with homes. The fact of having been in an approved school was mentioned by the boys in Northways very rarely, and no spontaneous mention was ever made of approved school staff. The occasional children's officer was mentioned in positive terms by the boys. The implication of this might be that the staffs of approved schools had not made significant relationships with the boys which carried through into their lives afterwards.

The boys who came to Northways had, on average, spent half their young lives in institutions (average 9·1 years), the longest of all being a boy, who, when admitted at nineteen, had been in institutions for over fifteen years. They had spent rather less time in borstal on average than had the homeless control, 15·5 months as against 17·4. Despite the already mentioned feeling of two boys that they had been kept in borstal in order to come to Northways it would appear that having somewhere to go reduced the time they actually spent in a borstal institution, although this may be a fortuitous finding.

EMPLOYMENT RECORD

Since ours was an open community it was clear, apart from any vocational assistance the boys might have received in borstal, that their previous employment record would be relevant both in demonstrating the value of their borstal experience and in helping us with our expectations of a given boy. We tentatively attempted to match job turnover in the three groups, but it is difficult to assess the reliability of the boys' statements, prior to conviction, about their employment. Ultimately the reliability of this against all available records will be checked. The boys tended while in Northways to underestimate the number of jobs they had while living there, and it is reasonable to suppose that this was not a new process for them. It seems likely that boys with a bad record of employment, suspicious of the motives of authority asking them about this, will exaggerate the period in which they had been in a single job and tend to forget their short-term jobs. They would also tend, we thought, to underestimate their periods of unemployment. The other difficulty in assessing work records was that some of the boys had spent a period of time in the Services and others had been at liberty for only very short periods of time. For example, in the Northways group one boy had lived in the

community for only six months from the age of fifteen. He spent
one month of this period in the army, so it was impossible to
make an adequate assessment about his employment record.
Another boy was at liberty from institutions for forty months,
but thirty-eight of these were in the navy, and one boy spent
thirty-nine of his forty-five months at liberty in the army. Of the
remaining eighteen boys, seven had more than six jobs per year,

TABLE 3   JOB RECORDS (CRUDE FIGURES)

	Northways	Homeless Control	Home Control
Boys excluded as less than 4 months as civilians or at liberty	3	3	1
More than 6 jobs per year	7	7	6
More than 3 jobs per year	8	14	17
More than 2 jobs per year	3	4	2
One job only per year	—	1	3
Unemployed more than 3 months per year	5	5	2
Unemployed more than 2 months per year	3	5	7

fifteen had more than three. The figures for the homeless control
group were quite similar, twenty-one out of twenty-nine had
more than three jobs a year; for boys with homes the control
figure was twenty-three out of twenty-eight (see *Table 3*).

Vocational training in borstal ought to have been helpful to the
boys in obtaining and keeping jobs. Nine of the twenty-one boys
of the Northways group had received vocational training in
borstal. Of the homeless control, vocational training had been
tried with ten out of twenty-nine; two had failed their courses, so
only eight had in fact received such training. For the group with
homes the number who received vocational training was seven
out of twenty-nine. This meant that somewhere between fifty to

seventy per cent of boys whose intelligence was high enough to train them for at least semi-skilled occupations were equipped only for unskilled labouring occupations. If vocational training is valued by the boys in borstals, then those who did not receive it would have reinforced their feelings of deprivation relative to others of a similar age and intelligence. This would seem to be particularly significant for the homeless groups, who felt themselves in any case to be underprivileged members of society.

PERSONALITY ASSETS

Prior to the opening of Northways we had considered what our goals might be. We had wished to create a situation in which a boy might have a greater opportunity of not being reconvicted and so we had hoped to help the group to become less antisocial and destructive to society at large. We knew that the boys were likely to be emotionally disturbed, but the severity of this came as a shock to us.

Normally these boys are seen by professional workers in the field as members of a larger group who are less disturbed than they. In institutions they are likely, because of their difficulty in making relationships, to become the quiet, unnoticed boy or the boy who is constantly getting himself punished. It is unusual for them to be related to as people by the staff. This type of boy does not normally present himself in out-patient psychiatric practice and if he does he usually does not continue with out-patient treatment. He becomes, we suspect, if he stays out of institutions, a member of that submerged ten per cent of society who use ninety per cent of the social services.

Our concept had been to help the group who came to Northways to become healthier and more mature people. The techniques we used have been broadly surveyed, but it was in our relationship with the boys that we hoped to improve their capacities as human beings. We have sketched out their emotional liabilities; if they were to be helped we also had to consider their assets.

Although their disabilities made it very difficult to relate to them and they seemed at times to do everything in their power to keep us at an emotional distance, most of the group were not unable to make a human relationship. The frustration in working with them was the necessity, as it seemed, to cover the same ground repeatedly. The central emotional position to which they constantly returned was one of denial, distrust, and depression. That they could be reached is demonstrable by a report on a house meeting. This took place shortly after one of their number had been picked up by the police for larceny.

When the psychiatrist arrived the boys were most reluctant to start the meeting and they drifted in grumbling about having to leave their girl-friends and having other things to do. They asked, 'What time do we finish?' They then went on to imply that it was good of them to attend the meeting and said to the psychiatrist 'What do you want to talk about?' The comment was made by the psychiatrist that if they had to make such an unusual song and dance about the uselessness of the meeting it must be most important to them; perhaps they were being diffident about 'what they wanted to talk about'. The boys then discussed the recent holiday, avoiding the subject of the boy who had been recently picked up by the police. Ultimately the interpretative comment was made that they must be very worried about J. since they had so obviously avoided mentioning him. This was greeted with a tirade of angry denial and in this they told of many horror stories associated with their treatment by officers in various institutions, implying that this had stopped them from repeating their crimes. They began to quarrel with each other about the value of being beaten up and two boys threatened to fight each other on the spot. At this point they were reminded that this sort of upset had not been seen for a long time. Perhaps they were not only afraid of what might happen to their friend, they were also afraid in case it happened to them. Surely their violence here and now showed how strongly they felt that violence did not help them control themselves in any way. At this point the tension subsided and they talked sadly about the other boy. They expected him to get three years and thought it would do no good at all.

Thus a most important asset was the boys' ultimate capacity to respond to an interpretative comment which conveyed understanding about what was happening to them. This was in no way associated with intellectual awareness on their part, and they were not able to verbalize any increased knowledge of themselves. This is explicable as, at such times as the boys could be emotionally contacted, repeatedly we ran into their basic depressive feelings which clearly were exceedingly painful to them. Sadness was a prevailing subtle motif throughout their lives.

Another asset that the boys showed was that they were able to turn to us for help on many occasions, provided we were alert enough to see that the request was more often made in behaviour than in words. Sometimes these signals were unavoidably missed:

One boy, shortly before committing a series of thefts, started, apparently out of the blue, to tell the assistant warden in a highly excited way about his previous crimes. The reason for this behaviour was not interpreted to him, as it was only with hindsight that it was recognized as an indication that the same thing was about to happen again. The next day he was picked up by the police, having broken into a house.

Although the boys' capacity to learn from experience was limited, it did appear to be present. Sometimes, although not always, a reminder to a boy that he seemed to be doing something to himself that he had done before was useful:

A boy who had repeatedly lost his job because of industrial dermatitis told the psychiatrist that he was going to get a job working in a machine shop. He was sensitive to oil. He was doing this, he said, to get the money to marry. An interpretation was made that in some way he must want to avoid marriage because he knew his hands and arms would break down if he took up such an occupation. He vowed he did not care and that it would not happen, but he did not take the job.

Although the boys had difficulty in using their intelligence, they were able to learn new skills both in work and in social relationships. From time to time they did begin to get glimmerings about other people's feelings:

> A boy went drinking with a recently married ex-Northways boy in a public house of which, unknown to him, the boy's wife disapproved. He said to the girl, 'Don't worry, we were only drinking in the local and I will look after him.' When he saw her distress he became acutely embarrassed. He said to the warden afterwards that he wished desperately that he had said nothing as he did not want to hurt the other boy's wife.

Another important asset was that gradually the boys began to be able to put feelings into words instead of acting upon them. This is demonstrable by the story of one boy in Northways. He openly felt that he had been damaged by his institutional life and yet he was able to yearn for its protection. 'I didn't want to leave borstal; I pretended I did, but it's safer inside, you know exactly where you are.' A progress report on him after three months by the psychiatrist was as follows:

> 'In a very early meeting he let me know how disturbed he was because he told me he had a history of having made a suicidal attempt when he was about fifteen. He also revealed that he had spent a period of time in a mental hospital and he expressed the wish to be back in borstal.
> 'Essentially he adopts a very passive role in relationship to one of his friends. In many group meetings in which they appear together they conduct a sort of duet. From time to time he withdraws from the group and from contact with me and one sees nothing of him for a couple of weeks at a time. He then returns, particularly if I indicate to him by some interpretative remark that his absence matters.
> 'He is quite a greedy boy in that he has borrowed more money from the loan fund than anyone else and he has found it

I

extremely difficult to return it. He told me when he saw me alone one day that he is drinking too much and he lets me know that he feels very troubled both internally and externally. Often he does this by talking of others, for example by casually mentioning that his married brother aged nineteen is in trouble. He has recently lost weight and looks distressed and he tends to get extremely agitated over rather minor discomforts.'

Although this boy could talk about his need to make Northways into a home, he was not able to contribute very much towards this constructively. He had done a good deal of job-switching, and his hypersuspicious anxiety was such that he was unable to say he was changing jobs until he had done so. Both in individual and group sessions this had been taken up with him, but it seemed always to be touch-and-go whether we could help him enough before he got into trouble again.

He developed a rather clinging and dependent relationship with the psychiatrist. Because it was clearly impossible to do intensive psychotherapy with any one boy in the house he was told that, if he agreed, arrangements might be made for him to be seen by another psychiatrist. He indicated that he did not think this was a bad idea, but he was unable to summon up enough resolution to ask that this be done.

This boy had been quite effective in his borstal, which clearly had provided him with support. It appeared that it had not helped him to resolve his propensity for turning his aggression against himself or others, nor had it helped in the resolution of his intense greed and dependency.

He made two suicidal gestures during his stay in Northways, one of which was certainly a real attempt, in that he took one-hundred aspirins believing that this was inevitably a lethal dose. On a third occasion, however, he was able to say to another boy at midnight, 'Please ask Dr. M. to come and see me, I feel terrible.' He was then able to talk about his wish to kill himself and put his depressed feelings into words. This capacity to put feelings into words depended to some extent on the stress the boys might experience. When this was acutely felt they tended to revert to a more primitive way of relating to their environment. At a later date the same boy felt that his manly feelings were threatened when a young supervising officer who was temporarily staying in the house told him, in front of his girl-friend, that he could not take her upstairs. He felt humiliated and impulsively attacked this man. Because of this he was recalled to borstal. His girl-friend continued to demonstrate her affection for him and visited him while he was there. His suspiciousness about human motivation had sufficiently abated for him to be able to be appreciative of this. After his return to the community he continued to visit Northways and ultimately he married, apparently highly successfully.

RELATIONSHIP BETWEEN PRE-BORSTAL AND NORTHWAYS ADJUSTMENT

It would seem not inappropriate to compare the clinical picture as recorded when the boys first appeared in the borstal allocation centre, with the picture as it presented to us in the assessment interviews in Northways. Although, on account of different types of reportage it is difficult to draw firm conclusions, our general impression was that, as far as the basic personality structure and attitudes of the boys were concerned, there had been no change.

It is theoretically valid on clinical grounds to assume that if the disturbed delinquent adolescent can firmly identify with an adult one may expect behavioural and attitudinal changes even if the fundamental psychopathology is untouched. If the institutional system can do anything valuable for its charges we would hypothesize that with their current resources of personnel they should provide identification models for their charges. There was no evidence in our group that this had happened. An eighteen and a half year old boy was reported upon at the borstal allocation centre in 1961 as follows:

Religion: Anglican.
Home: Mother, address not known. Lad no fixed abode.

Offence: Sacrilege.

Previous Convictions: Three:

Larceny: in charge of the Local Authority.

One year later: Larceny: Conditional Discharge.

Four years later: Larceny: Probation—twelve months.

Impression: About average intelligence and a bit backward in educational attainment. He is a lone wolf and seems to have no desire to settle and make roots. In interview co-operative, well behaved, light-hearted but such a 'will o' the wisp' it is difficult to get to grips with him. Pleasant, not bad material. Not in touch with anyone and has no plans but would like to live in London.

Home: He was born in L., his mother was described as a 'domestic worker' and name of father blank. He has heard that father was an American serviceman killed before he and mother could marry. From five months of age the lad has been with various foster-parents, in a Home from seven to fourteen, and in between has been to mother for short stays till she could farm him out again. From fourteen and a half to fifteen he has been to a College of Agriculture. Since then in B. in digs, in London two months. Mother has been living with a man for some years, they had been selling things at the seaside and in markets. A few years ago they put a large sum down on deposit for a cafe – chatter has it that the Income Tax people became interested in this sum available and they then did a moonlight flit. They have not been seen by the lad since and he has no idea where they may be. He says mother was fed up with him when he first got into trouble. To me it appears that the lad was a slip up and mother has done her best to farm him out all his life. Mother appears to have done herself fairly well, when the lad first slipped it was a good time to be upset and reject him. This lad appears to be undisturbed about the whole thing. As far as he knows there are no other children.

School: Main schooling at a residential school from seven to fourteen and a half and then an Agricultural College to fifteen. Says he is backward in arithmetic.

Work: About fifteen jobs, kitchen work and projectionist. Longest one year as projectionist from seventeen to eighteen. Last job kitchen porter two days till arrest. Pays £3. 10. for his board and lodgings. Longest spell of unemployment two months in a winter.

Health: Tonsils removed at eight. As far as known, four years ago, mother fit. Nothing known of father.

Interests: Swimming, the cinema, the theatre, mild drinking, smokes, no close friends, knows a few people. Two girl-friends have let him down so he has finished with girls. A Lone Wolf.

Delinquencies: Alone, all petty thefts until he stole £12 from lodgings in August. No excuses.

Religion: Attends church twice a year at Easter and Christmas.

Recommendation: Asks for bricklaying.

The Northways assessment was done ten months later and the psychiatrist's report read:

He is a rather well-spoken young man, quite tall; talks and dresses like a middle-class youngster. He had the compliant veneer which one has come to expect from these boys and one felt throughout the whole interview that one was talking to a recording machine rather than a human being. It was possible to talk to him about this and he said that in fact he had told his story so many times that it did not mean much to him any more. From time to time emotion was shown by a change of expression; e.g. when I mentioned that I was a psychiatrist; also at the point where he said that in a place like Northways one ought to have rules as to what time people should come in, and whether or not they were allowed to drink, and I put it to him that these rules did not exist. He said that he found this idea confusing.

The boy was apparently brought up by his mother until he was five months old and then he thinks he was placed with a family in B. He believes he lived with two families in all until he was five or six years old. He was then sent to a religious boys school where he stayed until he was fourteen. An attempt apparently was made then to place him in the Community but this did not work. He went back to the school for a while and then was sent to a farm school. The patient said that he had had numerous jobs but the only one he liked was as a cinema projectionist and he stayed at this longer than any other. At the moment he says that his borstal is quite a pleasant place. He seems to like the staff there, but he has no real friendships either with them or the other boys. He refers to himself as a lonely person. The borstal assistant governor tells him that he does not seem to get on well with the other boys.

He told me that he had in all three un-caught crimes, two of which were larceny, usually of small amounts of money from his employers. His first crime was stealing three pipes from Woolworths when he was fourteen and living in lodgings; because he refused to go to school at the time, the landlady called the police and he was given a conditional discharge. His second offence was stealing a bicycle; the same thing happened, and the third offence was larceny, for which he was put on probation.

He was finally committed to borstal for robbing a church offertory box. He is an Anglican and in fact robbed a church of that denomination. He said that while he was doing it he was very frightened and thinks that it was quite wrong.

There was something quite 'Pollyanna-ish' about the boy. He talked, for example, of having mixed with bad company. I got the impression that this was something that had been said to him rather than something he felt. I put this to him and he agreed. He said however that he did think that one should not mix with bad company because then you got led astray.

He told me he would like to be a bricklayer if possible. Failing this, he felt he would like to go back to being a cinema projectionist. He would like to become a foreman and that he would like to get married. I wondered if he had any problems with members of the opposite sex because of his early life, and he said that he felt exceedingly shy with girls and did not seem to be able to cope with them. He expressed repugnance and horror at the idea of any homosexual contact, although clinically he gives the impression of being slightly effeminate.

He then spontaneously mentioned his 'blackouts', which so far in fact have not been mentioned anywhere. According to him, when he was about fourteen or fifteen the matron at P. got angry with him and hit him on the head with a bunch of keys. He says that the key went into his skull – he seems only to have had first aid applied. However, whenever he is in a hot environment, which for him is unpleasant, he blacks out. He says that everything becomes blurred and dizzy. He has a temporary period of unconsciousness, but he is not incontinent. He was told by a doctor that these were hypotensive attacks but they seem never to have been investigated. He says that they occurred from time to time in borstal, but since he can usually grab on to something nobody notices them and he has never mentioned them. I asked him if he would mind if I mentioned this to Borstal After-Care and he said he would not.

The other thing which I noted about the boy was the extreme casualness with which he told me that various of his relatives were now dead; his mother, he thinks, and his grandparents, and he seems to have had no emotions about, for example, going to anybody's funeral.

This boy strikes me as being an 'as if' personality. He is exceedingly schizoid and I think is unable to establish a real relationship with anybody. In circumstances in which the demands of the external world are vague, he would appear to me to become clinically quite confused. His story of blackouts immediately following our discussion of relationships with girls coupled with the statement that these followed an attack by an older woman, would indicate the extent of his anxieties in relationship to the opposite sex. This is a boy however in whom one should eliminate the possibility of organic damage.

It is clear from these two reports that there was no clinical difference in the boy. What the psychiatrist described as 'schizoid', the borstal allocation report said 'such a "will o' the wisp" it is difficult to get to grips with him'. His stated goal had not changed and when he left borstal months after the Northways interview the position was still the same. As can be seen, quite properly his difficulties with relationships with the opposite sex were not mentioned in the borstal assessment.

In none of the twenty-one boys who came to Northways could we deduce, from a comparison between their written records and our clinical assessment, any evidence of improvement from their borstal stay. They seemed as emotionally unstable and unable to make satisfactory relationships on discharge as prior to committal. This can of course only be a deductive statement. A more careful assessment of the boys' personality prior to conviction and at discharge is required to assess whether or not it is significantly accurate for all borstal boys or just for those boys who enter borstal with evident psychological disturbance.

CHAPTER VIII

Therapeutic Techniques

Individual relationships

THEORETICAL BACKGROUND

IN THE creation of Northways we had in mind a family model, and it is appropriate to reconsider here what are the healthy assets in a family that are likely to make for the production of a well-balanced human being. Ideally, a child requires two parents, themselves reasonably mature, who should be able to provide an environment which is stable in a social sense. In addition, as a unit, the family needs to be a member of a larger stable social environment.

For the infant to develop satisfactorily he requires to be loved, to be treated consistently, and to be respected as a person. The latter entails that more (or less) is not expected at any stage of human development than the child can achieve and the expectations of the family group should take cognisance of the sex of the child. Girls should not be brought up as boys and vice versa. The family need to teach the child social performance that will take note of what they feel to be right and wrong. At the same time the good family implicitly recognizes the feelings of the child, enjoys its happiness, comforts its misery, and tolerates the normal anxieties associated with human growth and maturation. During adolescence the parents will recognize their offspring's growing need for independence and will respect the need for privacy. The adolescent should have the amount of social and personal responsibility he is able to handle. By this age necessary external controls should be provided basically on the strength of relationships within the family. Healthy families do not collude, either consciously or unconsciously, with the antisocial behaviour of their children. Neither do they put them in a situation in which there is a conflict of expectation; when one thing is said and another done.

A therapeutic environment cannot exactly reproduce the family situation, particularly with adolescents who are needing normally to become emotionally independent of parent figures. It should, however, be aware of and appropriately use the principles outlined above and, in addition, take note of the factors which had led, in the individual, to development becoming distorted. Often the typical institutional model does not do this. This is a function partly of the staff themselves becoming victims of a rigid institutional system, and partly of lack of training for them. For example, in recent years it has been generally understood in children's homes that, ideally, children separated from their parents need parent substitutes. It is unclear how effectively the subtleties of this are understood by the relevant staff. A memorandum or a short lecture course will not provide the necessary training skills. As a result, it is still too often ignored that children may enter a new environment in an emotional situation of anger, withdrawal, or both and require help to resolve the conflict that produces the anxiety behind these feelings. The over-quiet child or the child who latches on to each newcomer in a children's home may be as disturbed as the angry destructive child. If parental separation is not recognized as being, as is often the case, the prime trauma which these children have experienced, they approach adult life able to make only tentative relationships and easily wounded by, and hypersensitive to, repeated separation experiences.

There are several theoretical formulations about human development and the treatment of disturbed character formation. Our basic assumption was that there is a balance between the acting out of conflicts in society and the individual's ability to experience internal pain or anxiety in association with these conflicts. The less he is able to contain or sublimate the latter, the more the former will appear. The more, for example, a human being who has experienced the pain of separation creates relationships with others in which it is likely to occur again, paradoxically the less anxiety he will feel. It is as if the repetition of the situation represents an attempt at mastery. This allows the pain and anxiety to be tolerated because it is seen in relation to the other, rejecting, person, and not felt as belonging to oneself. If, on the other hand, the individual can be helped not reproduce this situation, he can then be helped in an interpersonal relationship. This is partly because he sees himself as needing assistance and is motivated to get it; partly because if he needs to act out less, his anxiety is more tolerable and thus can be experienced directly. People suffering from disturbed personality illnesses are often unable to wait for gratification, the insecurity of their early lives has been such that frustration is intolerable. Thus they appear selfish, greedy, and inconsiderate. If they can be assisted to contain these qualities within themselves, once again they become more susceptible to psychotherapeutic assistance.

In adolescents it is difficult to be sure why interpretations about the causation of any set of feelings or actions are helpful, but in fact it appears that gaining understanding of one's own motivation is of use. It may be, however, that in the most disturbed characters the understanding they perceive in other people may primarily assist them to make satisfactory identifications. They mature by becoming like the helpful person whose perceived qualities they appear to take into their own personalities.

There are several ways in which the internalization of difficulties can be achieved. The technique of rigid external control obviously prevents aberrant behaviour, but tends to result in the institutional reactions we have described. Theoretically, at the extreme, this type of approach so contains the individual that antisocial behaviour is impossible. However, without psychotherapeutic intervention no conflicts are likely to be resolved. Thus if a disturbed character is treated in such a system he will either break down when released from it, partly as an attempt to return to its security, or he will contain one type of disturbed behaviour only to produce another. It is unlikely that there will be sufficient personality growth to enable the individual to contain his own anxiety.

Many institutional staff are well aware that one of the disadvantages of the penal system as it currently operates is that, although it recognizes 'good' and 'bad' behaviour and applies rewards and punishment to these, often what is institutionally 'good' is not so in society at large. For example, the system of incentives may, and to an extent should, encourage conformist behaviour by rewarding it, but there is a risk that initiative, which in our society is also at a premium, cannot be rewarded so clearly. This good–bad dichotomy is the delinquent's system in any case; it is just that his vision of what is 'good' and 'bad' may not agree with the concepts of the larger body of society.

In Chapter I the point was made that adolescents need to have some feeling of external security. If the social system in which they live is over-permissive, then they will tend to set up rigid hierarchical systems of their own. Ideally a boy should have the amount of responsibility he is able to handle, but it should be given to him by adult society during the period of adolescence. If this is not done, then the adults are not seen as valuable and worthwhile models for identification.

This approach was implicit from the moment we had contact with a boy. In the assessment procedure we chose, in the first instance, whether or not the boy could go to Northways. Behind us in time was the borstal system saying, by implication, that the boy could now have the freedom to live in the community at large, given certain sanctions. Where we appeared to the boys to differ from the typical setting they had experienced was that we were demonstrably able to recognize the feelings of a given individual and convey understanding of any given piece of behaviour or attitude, while at the same time, if appropriate, registering our disapproval of it, more often in words than in deeds.

The group of staff working in Northways did not, as we have

said, have any real controls except the power to ask a boy to leave. If we were accurate in our assumption that the boys would attempt to reproduce the separation experience, then clearly this was a sanction we could rarely use. It was also clear that the boys would try many devices to avoid taking responsibility for their own fate and so far as possible we wanted them not to do this. In that the therapeutic situation started from the moment that the boy had contact with us; when the boys were told that they had a free choice as to whether or not they came to or stayed in the unit they were also told that they could tell us of their wish to leave in many ways. This could be done in words or actions and, in particular, if they persistently failed to pay their share of the cost of running the house, or they failed to come to the house meetings, we would take it that this was a message to us that they did not wish to stay.

The verbal recognition by a boy that he is responsible for a series of events may be fairly meaningless. For example, if in an approved school the social expectation of the system is that the boy should recognize his own part in any misdemeanour he will rapidly learn to do this as part of an institutional reaction. In that adolescence tends to be an age of action, and disturbed adolescents in particular are action-orientated, whenever possible such young people should have responsibility for what is going to happen, rather than just for what is said.

On one occasion a boy behaved very badly in the house in that he constantly 'borrowed' property from the assistant warden. He was jealous and envious of him, hence his aggressive behaviour, but it was clear that talking about his actions, at whatever level of understanding, did not change the issue.
Finally he was seen by the Director of Borstal After-Care which, since it was unusual, meant that his behaviour was being taken very seriously. He expected to be recalled to borstal at once, and was astonished when he was told that he must take the decision as to what would happen. After much discussion the boy expressed the feeling quite sensibly that going back to

borstal would solve nothing. To his surprise, the Director agreed with this, and the boy understood that he had a choice as to whether or not he would act in such a way as to demonstrate his need for recall in the future.

Since these boys had a weak ego, as controls could not be given by physical structure, then they would have to be maintained largely in the relationships we had with them and they had with each other. An example has just been given as to how we would use the 'magic' of the power held by external authority figures who were known to the boys as people but rarely seen by them. Nevertheless in general the social system we created would have to provide the subtle controls of having a way of life in which certain actions were acceptable, others unacceptable. It would also have to provide an emotional backcloth against which the boys would be helped to resolve their internal conflicts, develop a personality that could tolerate frustration, and have some feelings about the needs of others.

THE PROBLEM OF SEPARATION

The boys needed, because of their life experience of constantly losing parent figures, to be able to tolerate separation and to experience a feeling of loss, without acting out their rage and despair on the community at large. This meant that when they left the unit we would need to help them to understand their mixed feelings about this, as well as giving them the opportunity to keep in touch with us. For example:

> Just before a boy left Northways to go into the army he asked the psychiatrist whether he should 'go home to see his mother so that he could spend his leaves with her'. This was understood to mean that he wondered whether or not we still wanted him. The psychiatrist replied that he knew that the boy had never got on with his mother and doubtless this had not changed. He thought he ought to plan to spend his leaves in the unit. The boy was immensely relieved by this, wrote to the warden quite

regularly, spent his leaves at Northways, brought his fiancée to stay nearby when he was on leave, and finally married from the house.

If a boy was leaving when he consciously felt ready to do so, although there was evidence of separation anxiety, the situation was not as complex as if he left because the staff felt he was ready to go. Some of the boys had such intense dependency needs that we obviously could not expect them to initiate their own departure, particularly if leaving the house meant that they would have to move into lodgings. There was no fixed time-limit during which a boy should stay, but in fact when they reached the age of twenty-one they were starting to become in many ways more 'adult' than the rest of the group. We made a decision that a boy should leave if we felt that he was capable of working out a separation experience without needing to react by criminal behaviour in the community at large, if he demonstrated a capacity to work at a job, and if he was able to make relationships with members of the opposite sex. Another criterion was that his institutional reactions should have disappeared and that he should be able to put his difficulties into words to people whom he perceived as having authority over him; in other words, he had to be less paranoid and hyper-suspicious. By the end of a two-year period, the group of boys evidently realized that there was an expectation that they would be ready to live in the larger community soon after passing the age of twenty-one. They had mixed feelings about this: partly they felt it to be desirable; partly they did not wish to go. The possibility of living outside the house was in any case implicit in the structure; 'When you live in lodgings', or 'When you marry', was often said by the staff as part of our attempt to keep the boys outer-directed. Another criterion for leaving was the staff's assessment that we had done as much as was possible for any individual boy with the resources available. An example of the technique is as follows:

A boy of twenty-one had been in Northways about eighteen months. During that time he had demonstrated a capacity to work and had acquired a girl-friend, even though it was clear that there was little depth to the relationship. He was able, with difficulty, to remain honest if he was out of a job, and no longer appeared to be in a perpetual state of anxiety about authority and what it might do to him. He was unreliable with money, often borrowing it from a friend and not returning it. He demonstrated minimal capacity to care for other boys in the house, and we believed that he was responsible for taking some of their clothes and selling them. He was prepared to work in the house, which seemed often to be a manipulative attempt to buy affection. He tended to somatize his anxiety.

We did not believe that his stay in the unit had resolved the problem of his basic coldness, but it seemed likely that his judgement was now sufficiently sound and that he was unlikely to break the law. We thought that if he could understand how some of his hostile behaviour was related to his wish to be dependent, and the frustration of that, he might make a reasonable community adjustment. He was told in a group meeting one evening that the psychiatrist expected that he would be thinking of moving out into the community in the next six months or so. He agreed with this, but shortly thereafter lost his job and seemed to be involved in a series of minor thefts from the other boys. The psychiatrist interpreted to him that he was anxious about leaving and was trying to show that he was not ready to do so. The boy responded with fury and said, 'You can throw me out if you want to.' The reply was that this is what he was most afraid about and the boy stormed from the room. He then missed two group meetings and was told, 'You are trying to get me to throw you out; if you want to go now you can, but, I think you should stay at least another three months, then you must be ready to move.' The boy angrily replied that he had not yet lived in the house two years, therefore the psychiatrist had no right to suggest this. He complained to the warden and in the house meeting that the psychiatrist was 'trying to chuck me out'. He said it was never discussed with him; then he failed to pay his rent. The warden commented to him that he was saying he wanted to stay but acting as though he wished to leave. She thought he should stay the three months so he could leave in a settled way.

All this aroused great anxiety among the other boys. One had to be convinced that saving money would not mean his immediate ejection, another who was destructive under stress demonstrated his 'strength' by moving a large piece of kitchen equipment. In the group many interpretations were made about the anger and anxiety of the boys as it related to their present and past experience of separation.

Our basic attitude was that however much the boy acted out his anxiety in the house he had to leave at the end of the time stated. We intended to convey to him our understanding of his distressed and disturbed behaviour in the house, but if his upset made it possible for him to stay longer we felt that the secondary gain would be such that his chances of leaving and making a successful life adjustment would be minimal. In fact, he did move out finally as a result of neglecting to pay his rent, and for more than one year he has continued to make a sufficiently good adjustment for reconviction to seem unlikely. From time to time he has had contact with the psychiatrist; on one occasion, when the possibility of hospitalization was discussed with him following temporary unemployment, he rapidly found a job. He has maintained contact with his supervising officer, and it is thought that even when his supervision expires he will continue to do so.

With this boy, as with others in the same situation, our opinion that he was ready to leave Northways was conveyed to him, in the first instance, by the psychiatrist. In his eyes this made the psychiatrist both responsible and 'bad', a situation which could be dealt with in the transference relationship; the warden was more likely to be consciously perceived as 'good' and thus could continue to give him direct emotional support in what was, for the boy, a period of great anxiety.

The staff had, then, to be seen by the boys as consistent, reliable, likeable, understanding people. Whether or not they would be able to exercise control through the strength of their relationship with the boys would depend on their personality and their motivation, but they would also need specific training. In addition to the individual relationships which might assist in building acceptable social behaviour into the environment, there would also be the group interaction processes of the boys with each other and the staff in both formal and informal situations. By the former are meant the specific house meetings; by the latter, 'family' type groups such as meal-times, in which the boys and the staff would together discuss the running of the house and various aspects of their lives.

The training role of the psychiatrist has already been mentioned. One of the problems of trying to enhance psychosocial sophistication is that people may become less spontaneous during the process. They may be inhibited by over-anxiety as to whether or not they are reacting appropriately. This can be avoided if they do not feel emotionally pushed and if they are adequately supported, in that more is not expected of them at any one time than they can achieve. On occasion errors were made, and the following example demonstrates what occurred when too much was expected too rapidly. As will be seen, the problem was a similar one, at a different level, with the staff worker and with the boy.

The aim was to help the staff member to be seen as a firm, consistent, understanding person who would not expect from a boy more than he was capable of producing, both socially and emotionally. The intention was to help the boy to feel less anxious and to behave as a more independent person. The boy was described to the staff member, by the psychiatrist, as follows:

This is a nineteen-year-old boy of average intelligence who potentially can function at a much higher level but his emotional difficulties inhibit this. His intelligence quotient is actually 103, potentially between 115 and 125. He desperately needs to feel love and affection, and one of the ways in which he tries to get them is by trying to find out what authority wants and giving it to it. He will thus say 'yes' when he means 'no'. Another way of putting it is to say that he sacrifices a long-term goal for an immediate satisfaction. He cannot tolerate frustration and gets distressed and anxious when confronted with it. He has difficulties in making close relationships. There is evidence that he has had some homosexual anxieties, although none at this moment that he has been involved in such activity.

This description of the boy was possible because of the assessment techniques we had used, although we were somewhat hampered by his failure to keep his second psychological test appointment. Some ten days after he came to the unit the following incident happened:

He had arrived home bringing the balance of his pay, £3. 11s. which he had given to the staff member to cover his lodgings for the week. In his case the sum had already been paid by the Borstal After-Care authorities and the money was consequently available for him to spend. He drew thirty shillings to cover his weekend expenses, and it was suggested to him that the rest of the money should be rationed out to him at the staff's discretion. The boy had said 'yes' with enthusiastic agreement.

Up to this point it was clear that the staff member had not really heard the psychiatrist talking with him about the boy. His 'training' image was that children are taught by the process of being externally controlled. He was not aware that a child must have positive feelings for the parent or parent-surrogate for this technique to be meaningful. Thus, although he intellectually understood the boy's passivity, he did not apply his understanding in terms of his interaction with the boy and was satisfied to accept the 'yes'.

By Sunday evening the boy had run out of money and he asked the staff member for some more. The response was to tell him that he had agreed that it should be rationed out, and the money was refused. The boy became furious, threatened violence, and next day came to see the psychiatrist complaining that his money had been taken from him, 'He's a thief.'

If the boy had had a stronger ego it might have been possible to talk about the situation and make no specific recommendation for action. In the psychiatrist's judgement the boy could not be helped enough by verbal interchange to be able to tolerate the frustrating implication of his agreement. If he could not be literally helped out of his dilemma it was thought likely that he would either disintegrate psychologically or more probably steal again with an inner feeling of complete justification. We would have no way of stopping either. The staff member had reason to say, 'The boy has said something and must learn to stick to it.' On the other hand, the boy was so confused and paranoid that in his own mind the whole story was now distorted. The reality of the situation had lost its meaning for him, and his level of anxiety was such that any interpretation of what he had created, without offering him a chance of retrieving the here-and-now situation, would not be helpful. If the psychiatrist had done as the boy wished, and had intervened to make the staff give him 'his money', clearly the boy's unconscious manipulative aims would be reinforced. It would be as if the psychiatrist agreed with him that the staff member was 'bad'.

The boy poured out his tale of woe, and when his tension had somewhat subsided it was possible to make an interpretative comment to him about his passivity and his living for the minute, his 'yes' was an attempt to get the staff member to like him. When he agreed with this the psychiatrist commented that neither he nor the boy could know whether this 'yes' technique was not going on at the very moment. The boy reverted to talking of the badness of the staff member, and the psychiatrist suggested that it was clear not only that the attempt to be 'good' had misfired, but also that the boy equally disliked his present position. Surely, then, the boy's problem now was to go back home to Northways and face the fact that he should not have said 'yes'. He would have to ask again for his money. If he got it, he must know that if he ran out again it was his own problem and not one for which he should be able to blame others.

The boy then returned to see the staff member, and the psychiatrist rang the latter to explain what had happened. He suggested to him that it was possible to play into the more infantile side of the boy's personality and really try to protect him by not giving him the money. The problem here was that the boy could only see this as cruel and persecuting. Alternatively, we could attempt to gratify his more mature wishes by giving him the responsibility for himself, although it was doubtful whether he knew any more than 'this is mine, I want it'. In discussing this the psychiatrist ignored the fact that the staff member's anxiety in the new situation was such that he had not been able really to understand what had been conveyed to him in the first instance. Thus the response was, 'Oh well, we'll let him do what he likes and then we'll get rid of him.'

The staff member had a personality which led him to relate to the boys in a somewhat judgemental manner, to prove that they had been 'good' or 'bad'. He found it hard to empathize with their feelings and understand their difficulties. To him such responses meant that one could not at the same time express or show disapproval, nor, if one had authority, that one could exercise it.

This failure on the part of the psychiatrist to take adequate note of the staff member's ability to learn at a comfortable rate for himself led to the very situation which it was desirable to avoid. The staff member now felt uncertain what to do and self-conscious about himself. Since he felt that the psychiatrist had disapproved of his first interaction with the boy, he now felt unable to act without the former's permission. This reaction is, of course, similar to that which a boy might have in an equivalent situation.

One afternoon, one of the group of boys from a borstal which was responsible for decorating the house absconded. He took some clothes from the house and a grip belonging to the boy who has just been discussed. This was later found under some floorboards. The staff member felt unable to ask the boy about this until he had checked with the psychiatrist that he might, and he took no constructive action until he had done so.

Thus the aim of having the staff member seen as a 'firm, understanding, consistent person' did not succeed in this whole episode. He felt so insecure that he could not relate to the boy with comfort. The boy continued to see him as alternatively rigid or demanding or over-permissive. At that time in the history of the house the staff member's security and ability to learn were of the highest importance, and it might have been better if no attempt had been made to resolve the situation with the boy in the way just described. We were perhaps in a situation in which there had to be a choice between the emotional security and growth of a member of the staff and that of a boy. Unconsciously the psychiatrist chose the latter. It may be that the staff member's perception of this led to the fact that for a very long time he was not at ease with either the boy or the psychiatrist.

An essential aspect of training is that a staff member should be able to feel that what he does is valuable and that the native abilities he brings to a situation are worth something in themselves. If he feels this, he is less likely to become anxious. A staff member learning new and more sophisticated techniques is particularly liable to lose spontaneity when aggressive feelings are being expressed by a boy and are also felt as a reaction within himself. Often the psychiatrist's own responses were used by him to demonstrate this type of problem. He might tell the staff of his own aggressive feelings aroused by a boy's aggression and explain why he had reacted in the way he did. The episode when a boy brushed his coat over the psychiatrist in a group meeting (see p. 68) in which the response was 'I wonder why you need to pour "dirt" over me?' was discussed with the staff. It was pointed out that one could have replied to the action by telling the boy to stop it directly, or by criticizing him. This would have aroused increasing defensiveness in the boy and nothing might have been resolved.

Another supportive technique, already mentioned in terms of the boy's separation anxiety, was for the psychiatrist to put himself in the position in which the boy's anger was directed at him. Thus the staff could continue to be perceived as part of the good external world.

In the process of building acceptable behaviour into the social system it was finally agreed in the house group at large that physical violence was unacceptable. Also no boy would have sexual intercourse in the house and no girl would be taken upstairs to the bedrooms. If these house rules were broken, perhaps as part of a testing-out situation, all the staff felt that we might have to ask a boy to leave, for the common good, although we did not wish to reject him in any final way. He could return to the house to visit or talk to the staff and boys.

At a meeting between the staff and the psychiatrist one Sunday morning the latter was told that one of the boys had brought his girl-friend in to sleep. Apparently he had appeared to leave with her at eleven o'clock the night before, but next morning she was sleeping in the spare room. Both the warden and her assistant were angry about this. The psychiatrist suggested that the boy should be asked to come up to see him in the warden's flat. When the boy came in he was told in front of the warden that his behaviour was quite unacceptable and that he would have to find himself a room at once. The warden intervened to inquire whether the boy might have a week to do so, if he had nowhere to go. He was also obliged to inform his supervising officer of the change. The psychiatrist's reply, in front of the boy, was that if this was necessary he would certainly agree, but that the boy could not stay beyond the week.

He told the boy that he apparently had needed to demonstrate his anger and contempt in this manner but it was not a helpful way of proving his own manhood. The boy, normally an openly aggressive youngster, was extremely chastened. He indicated that he did have somewhere to go and he left the house the next morning.

This interaction was designed to show the staff that it was acceptable to use aggressive feelings in a constructive way. In this case the psychiatrist used the power to cause a boy to leave, over an episode of sexual behaviour. About a year earlier the warden had behaved similarly when one boy hit another. The present action was supportive to the staff because this was an extremely aggressive boy and his hostility about being 'thrown out' was maximally directed towards the person he saw least, the psychiatrist, and minimally towards the staff, who would certainly see much of him.

The boy's 'good–bad' approach to life meant that it was important that he should continue to see the warden as good. If he had consciously felt her to be 'bad', he would then have had little emotional support in what was for him a crisis, and it would have been difficult for him to use Northways in a helpful way in the future.

This worked fairly well; he 'accidentally' broke a window in the front-door of the house the following week, but he continued to make adjustment in society and continued his relationship with his girl-friend, whom he ultimately married.

An immediate gain was obtained for staff training, and an established code of sexual behaviour was maintained in the house. Since we had to control the boy by the use of a rejection technique, an effort was made to ensure that he could still get help from the staff. As we might have expected, controlling the manifestations of aggressive behaviour in one area of the boy's social functioning, without resolving his underlying conflict, led to its appearance elsewhere. Nevertheless, the boy did not lose his job, nor did he react to the situation with recidivism.

THE THERAPEUTIC ROLE OF THE WARDEN

To the untrained person it is most difficult to convey the balance between control, empathic understanding, and interpretation, a combination which requires a high degree of psychotherapeutic skill. In the following situation, in which a boy became involved in a psychotic-like positive-transference situation, the warden was able to interpret a boy's unconscious hostility with ultimately markedly successful results.

An eighteen-year-old boy was admitted to the house with a combination of an appalling history of maternal deprivation and a crime record which consisted only of an attempted breaking and entering to get food. He was like a tormented and wounded being. He seemed unable to make relationships with anyone. He was one of the boys who said of his borstal experience, 'They said I did not do well because I could not get on with the other lads.'

For his first six months in the unit he held an unpleasant manual job with very poor pay. In most meetings he was quite inarticulate. He had bizarre food fads and lived for months on a diet that consisted largely of beans. Often he would not eat in the presence of the other boys, and his sole comments to the psychiatrist were to say he was 'all right, thank you'. At first he related only to the male staff member. Ultimately he responded to the consistent steady firm kindness from the warden, who would express interest in what he was doing, encourage him to social activity of various types, and look after his physical well-being. He appeared not to have a friend outside the house. As he began to respond to the warden he became more and more demanding of her time and energies and he showed increasing jealousy of her daughters and of other boys.

At this point, after discussing the position with the psychiatrist, she was able to say to the boy that she knew how much he wanted to be cared about, but, because she could never replace a real mother, he was extremely angry with her. He was showing this by trying to create a situation in which she would have to reject him. The boy settled down and he was able to spend a weekend away from the house with a distant relative. At a later date he wondered with the male staff member whether one should fall in love with an older woman and he was told 'no'.

Some time later the whole situation began to repeat itself. Once again the warden was able to make interpretations to the boy about his aggressive clinging behaviour. At one point when it was clear that the boy was struggling with most intense feelings she was able to make a remark that was both extremely helpful and controlling. Over a holiday weekend she told him that she insisted that he should go away for a holiday. He was being so insistent in his demands that she could not continue to meet his reasonable needs without a rest. She pointed out to him that he could, if he so wished, prove to himself that she was as bad as he felt all other women in his life to have been, by getting her to want nothing to do with him. She suggested that he took the weekend off to think about it. Once again he settled down in his relationship with the warden.

On this occasion his behaviour came up in a house meeting. As part of a process of wondering why, as a group, they were being so inarticulate, one boy said ' . . . You never talk.' He denied this, but then the boys complained to him, 'You spend hours with Mrs. D., you are jealous when we want to talk to her, why don't you spend more time with us; then you will spend less with her and we won't feel all the time you are talking about us.'

Without the work put in by the warden the boy could not, it appeared, have tolerated such a remark.

In fact, he became thoughtful and reflective and said, 'I suppose you are all right. It's just that I'm shy.' This represented a turning-point in the boy's adjustment, and steadily his relationships began to mature. He first began to live vicariously, enjoying the overt hostility of others, but he got a better job and became less infantile in his relationships.

This summary of what happened with one boy can only hint at the difficulty of the warden's task. She had to tolerate the attention-getting greed not only of this boy but of many others as well. Her ability to handle these feelings would seem to demonstrate the value and success of the learning process, the team approach, and the help she got from the psychiatrist; furthermore, she did not lose her natural feelings in her relationships with the boys.

TEAM RELATIONSHIPS

If a team project is successful, various members of the team tend to function in ways that fit with each other. A stage is reached at which, with no special discussion, different people can make accurate interpretative or supportive comments which lead to a dovetailing of effort. An example of this was as follows:

A smooth-spoken, rather suave young man of twenty was rejected by his mother when he was two. He was illegitimate, and after experiencing two foster-homes, at the age of five or six, he was sent to a religious boarding-school run by women. There he remained for nine years. Subsequently he lived in various lodgings and ultimately he was in borstal for nearly two years.

In his initial interview with the psychiatrist he denied any sexual difficulties. After a short period of comparative quietude when he came to the house, he was extremely restless and talked of leaving and changing his job. He tried to grow a beard. The warden constantly encouraged him to keep his job. When he impulsively gave notice to leave, she persuaded him to ask his employer to keep him in the firm. She behaved quite unlike a landlady of his middle adolescent years who had thrown him out of the house for a similar action. At the same time in the group meetings he was becoming increasingly sad. On one occasion when the psychiatrist was sitting on the arm of a chair he sat down in it and put his head on the former's shoulder like a small child. At the next meeting he asked if he could see the psychiatrist alone.

He opened the interview by saying he was terribly frightened because he was so restless and easily irritable. The psychiatrist wondered what was disturbing him to make him feel that way, and he said, 'You remember the question you asked me when you saw me at the Clinic – I lied to you because I was scared of what you would think.' Although the psychiatrist felt that the boy must have been referring to a question about homosexuality, he replied, 'Perhaps you would like to tell me now.' The youngster then went on to tell a story of being made to masturbate an older man when he was about seven. Then he told a story of being picked up by a homosexual on Waterloo Station when he was seventeen. 'You know what that place is like; I was very naïve and when a man offered me a bed, since I had nowhere to go I went back to his flat with him. There were two men and two beds and he suggested I share his. I was a bit worried but, after all, it was two men, wasn't it, and that's not so unusual? When I was half asleep he started to play with me and I liked it and let him. Then he buggered me and it hurt, but I liked that too. Then I did the job and got sent to borstal.' The boy went on to say that he spent his time thinking about men and was terribly tempted to commit a crime again so 'I can go back to borstal, it's safe there; the boys called me Mary, but I didn't mind.'

The psychiatrist told him that he would try to arrange for him to be seen regularly by another doctor, and interpreted to him his feelings about the fact that he himself had not offered to do so. He also commented, after some further discussion that made it clear that this was in the boy's mind, that he would for a short while be even more tempted to run away, 'I know you want help, but you are afraid of what goes on inside you.' The boy said he knew this but he had to be helped, 'Otherwise I can never marry and lead a decent life, and I can't be lonely all the rest of my days.'

The warden knew nothing of this conversation. All through the following week the boy kept talking of leaving the unit so that his supervising officer would not know where he was. She kept commenting to him that he was obviously trying to run away from himself, which was impossible, and, further, that she thought he ought to stay. He quit his job during this period but remained in the house. After the next group meeting the boy again saw the psychiatrist, who said, 'I am sure that you must be very frightened of the idea of treatment and are making it as hard for yourself as you can.' The boy agreed, saying, 'Yes, I've been making it very difficult for Mrs. D., too. I've been treating her as if she were to blame for what my mother did to me.'

With individual boys one had to be patient, controlling, supportive, and understanding. Just as from time to time one or other of the staff had to make interpretations to the boys, at others they had to directly intervene in their lives. Sometimes the boys would appear to be using Northways merely as a place to sleep. In such situations events showed that our failure to reject them, and our willingness to offer them support whenever they needed it, paid a helpful dividend.

A boy of eighteen when seen in initial interview was so frightened of the implications of the psychological tests that in a panicky anxious manner he refused them. It appeared that mostly he was anxious about his own sexual feelings, particularly as he had been involved in a series of sexual episodes in early adolescence for which he had been convicted.

At first when he came to the unit, he was very dirty. He did not observe even the most superficial of institutional habits, good manners at table and cleanliness. He was subject to ungovernable rages, which he finally began to recognize as constituting his own problem. Originally these had appeared in the house meetings when someone had said something which he perceived as slighting, and in interviews with the psychiatrist he was able to say how frightening they were to him.

Rapidly he found himself a girl-friend with whom finally he spent a great deal of time. It appeared to us that he was using the house as a transit camp.

He was colourfully described by a temporary staff member as follows: 'For the first few weeks he struck me as the dirtiest, laziest, most foul-mouthed, cowardly youth I have ever met. There was only one point about him which I admired: this was the fact that when I criticized these qualities he bore no grudge. Our constant clashes have eventually established a relationship of sorts, and I have begun to see him in a different light. Underneath the aggressive, foul-mouthed front he is a lost but quite likeable little boy; he is desperate to find an anchor and may well marry at the first opportunity.' Ultimately his relationship with his first girl-friend ended. He was extremely distressed by this.

The psychiatrist had to intervene with her family who were accusing him, quite inaccurately, of rape.

The staff and the psychiatrist had a primarily supportive relationship with him, which involved repeatedly telling him what he ought to do and pointing out to him the implications of what he did. When he wanted finally to go into the army, and was temporarily rejected because he had held no one job long enough, he was constantly encouraged to hold his job. Ultimately he was accepted by the forces. One year after he left he continued to do well. He came back to Northways for his embarkation leave and for a home leave one year later. Six months after this, having applied to the courts for permission, he married.

In reviewing ideal family structure, the point was made that control is possible through the strength of relationships. In a social system such as is being described the staff inside the house had authority similar to that of the parents of late adolescents. As has been said, they could ask the boys to leave. With the extreme personality instability of the boys, it is evident that more direct control might be needed, and this was provided by the supervising officer.

There is always the risk that the presence in a team of one member with specific legal authority and responsibility might be used by the other members. To do so would only reinforce the boys' tendency to split the world into good and bad; quite apart from the fact that it would also disintegrate the whole process in which the people involved with the boys worked together, just as, in a family group, the persistent use by one parent of another as a threat is disintegrative. In any case, the boys easily became hyper-suspicious and thus, if we were sufficiently sensitive, we would never permit a situation in which any member of the staff would use the supervising officer as a threat. We were, however, well aware that his specific authority had meaning for the boys. If, for example, a boy had wild plans to leave town, the warden might ask him if he had mentioned them to his supervisor. Similarly, if a boy was passively failing to find a job, the supervisor would be asked to discuss the situation with him.

We knew that on his routine visits he would do so anyway, but we would convey to him our view that the boy needed a specific push from an authority figure with real power.

Apart from this, the supervising officer conducted skilled supportive casework with the boys. He did not make interpretations about what the boy was doing in the transference relationship with him, although occasionally he would comment about this element in his relationships with others. He represented a 'caring-for' authority. Often he helped the boys with their real-life dilemmas; job-finding when they could not do so themselves and the other staff were unable to help; providing funds for clothing and tools; and, not least, being interested in them and spending time with them.

More effort and energy were expended on our group by the supervising officer than is usually possible. Because money is given only after considerable discussion with a boy, the sum spent by Borstal After-Care on the group as compared with the homeless controls is an indicator of the degree of attention. Over a period of two and a half years the boys in Northways had loaned to them an average of £21. 2. 6d. each, with repayments averaging £2. 18. 9d. each. Only five boys in the Northways group received this help for more than five months. Their average is pushed up because one highly disturbed boy received £63. 4. 11d. over the period, and another boy who had his fares subsidized for five months received £41. 8. 0d. The homeless control group had an average of £8. 14. 6d. each loaned to them; out of the total sum only £3. 5. 0d. was returned.

Because, during their stay in the unit, the boys became less suspicious of the motives of authority, it can be deduced that authority was wisely used in a helpful way. The important feature is that there was no attempt at punishment by authority figures. In the boys' minds several important clarifications began to take place. They began to see that there is a difference between being punished by external authority and being controlled by it. They also modified their 'we–they, good–bad' attitude to life and their initial view that in some way authority figures were better than they and also to be envied.

CHAPTER IX

Therapeutic Techniques

The group process

THE GROUP processes of Northways were an important part of the psychosocial therapeutic environment. Some of these, as we have said, were informal: the effect of the boys on each other, the relationships in day-to-day living between the resident staff and the boys, as they arose in eating meals with them, working and playing games with them, talking with them as a group, or merely being prepared to sit with them watching television. More formal group techniques were used by the psychiatrist in his relationship with the boys. In the weekly house meeting the boys were told that the discussion could be completely free. The boys could say whatever they liked with the knowledge that it would be confidential unless they wanted it otherwise, but there was no implication that they could do what they liked, and this was made quite explicit. The meeting was to last one and a half hours, and the expectation was that all the boys resident in the house would attend. We believed that the meetings would be therapeutically useful, economical in time, and possibly effective in helping the boys to resolve some of their difficulties with the world at large, with each other, and with themselves as individuals. The process might also be helpful in disseminating certain attitudes throughout the house. The intention was that this more formal group should supplement individual relationships with the boys, not that it should replace them.

With the use of formal group techniques it is easier than in one-to-one relationships to help some individuals to recognize their denial of their own internal difficulties. This is particularly the case with people who project their own anxieties on to the outside world, a typical delinquent mechanism, and with those who focus all their internal difficulties on a given set of symptoms – sufferers from psychosomatic illnesses, alcoholism, and drug addiction. For example:

> A group of university students recommended for group therapy because of work difficulties were most doubtful of its value. After two sessions they were talking freely of their inner emotional problems, in particular their awareness of their sexual maladjustment.

The group of boys who lived in Northways had not had the experience, which is typical for middle-class youth, of one-to-one relationships being highly important. Group living tends to be the norm in the social group from which they came. Among the middle classes one-to-one relationships and privacy tend to be valued from infancy. It is more usual for the middle-class mother to feed her child in a room away from the family than it is for the working-class mother, who is more likely to feed her child quite comfortably amidst the whole family group. Furthermore, since the boys had had many years of the group living involved in institutional experience, in which even going to the lavatory is often not private, it appeared more likely that one-to-one relationships would be perceived as chastising. To some extent, interviews with authority figures in their lives had often had this connotation. If the boys could become comfortable with each other and the staff in formal and informal group settings we believed that it was more likely that they would be able to make significant interpersonal relationships.

If our population had been girls, the group process would not have been used by us in the same way. Boys find it easy to make larger peer-group relationships; from an early age girls are more interested in one-to-one relationships, and their spontaneous groupings are more likely to be in a series of pairs.

Growth to Freedom

Without question there are fashions in psychosocial medicine. Since Maxwell Jones's work on the 'Therapeutic Community'[1] and the influence of the Tavistock group in England[2] and of Slavson[3] and his co-workers in the U.S.A., group therapy and, or, counselling has been the vogue. One of the problems created by such fashions in a society such as that in Great Britain, in which only very recently has expertise become somewhat valued, is that all too often techniques are applied by untrained or semi-trained personnel. As a result, after a number of years, an inadequately applied process may be studied, found wanting, and then either modified or dropped. Historically this is what seems to have led to criticism of the whole borstal system. This appears to be one of the factors which led to the introduction, in the author's view, of the initially sociologically regressive detention centre.

The issue is important because, just as we had to consider the placing of the community in society at large, so we had to consider the placing of the techniques that we were to use in the same context. Our carefully considered use of group work to some extent represented a social aberration. We believed that group work cannot be done without very adequate training, in which the worker also has understanding of individual personality development and individual therapeutic techniques. It is probably more difficult to respond adequately to aggression from eight people than from one.

The many types of group therapy have received many labels: group counselling, group psychotherapy, group analysis. Group interaction processes are also used for the training of personnel in psychotherapeutic techniques such as casework. It is appropriate to consider what type of group work we envisaged.

From time to time the word 'transference' has been used throughout this study and it may well be redefined at this point. Transference is taken to mean the reawakening in a present inter-

[1] Jones, M. *Social Psychiatry*. London: Tavistock Publications, 1952; as *The Therapeutic Community*, New York: Basic Books 1953.
[2] Bion, W. R. *Experiences in Groups and Other Papers*. London: Tavistock Publications, 1960; New York: Basic Books.
[3] Slavson, J. R. *Introduction to Group Therapy*. N.Y.: The Commonwealth Fund, 1943.

personal situation of emotional conflicts from the individual's past which affect the way he perceives, feels, and makes a relationship. The other person is related to not just as he or she really is, but also as if this was a significant figure out of the experience of the individual. This very wide definition would apply to all interpersonal situations. Thus, with the boys in Northways, authority figures of either sex might be related to as if they were the hurtful and rejecting parent. This concept, which is meaningful, can presuppose a rigidity in making relationships on the part of disturbed individuals. One way of looking at the goal of the project is to say that the aim was to correct this type of emotional perceptual distortion.

In therapeutic situations transference may be enhanced in a variety of ways, creating a 'transference neurosis'. If, for example, a patient is placed on a couch in psycho-analysis, it seems likely that, because he does not see the reactions of his analyst, who is not known as a real person, the analyst is even more likely to be seen as a figure out of the patient's experience than as a real person. If interpretations are made about this, the process is likely to be enhanced for the patient and he becomes aware of his inner conflicts about himself and his relationships with others. If a patient is seen every day, if he has no people in his life other than his therapist, he is likely to become over-involved in the treatment situation, which may become sterile and non-productive. The intensity of the transference neurosis is modified by the strength of the patient's ego; the weaker it is, the less adequately can a transference neurosis be handled by the patient.

This theoretical discussion is relevant to how Northways and the group process were to be used. The boys came to the house with effectively no real relationships in the outside world. Not one boy had a girl-friend from his pre-borstal experience; the three boys who had a living parent with whom they were in contact had such an ambivalent relationship with them that they all discontinued a tenuous effort to spend any time with them. If Northways became too inward-looking and if too intense an effort was made to have the boys consider their own inner world, it appeared likely that they would be unable to make significant relationships with anyone in the community at large. For this reason the house meeting was held only once a week and a great deal of effort was made by the staff to have the boys become outer-directed to the community at large rather than inner-directed towards themselves and each other. There was no wish to replace one type of institutional over-dependence with another. This was particularly the problem with those boys who had spent a long time in closed institutions. A high wall provides a false feeling of security both for the individual within it and for society at large; it does not prepare people to make relationships in the real world and tolerate the stresses of living.

A group therapist may function in a group in a variety of ways. Comments that he makes as to what the individual is unconsciously experiencing in the immediate relationship with the therapist constitute a 'transference interpretation'. It may be phenomenological, related to the here-and-now situation, or it may also be related to the person's past experience. An example of the need for an interpretation is as follows:

It is not uncommon for a boy in an institutional setting to ask a young staff member whether or not he has premarital intercourse.

In some settings this is taken as undue familiarity, and the boy is punished for rudeness. In more understanding situations the question may be directly answered. Both are probably inadequate responses. Taking the transference situation into consideration, it could be hypothesized that, as part of his wish to establish his own masculine security, the boy is really wondering what the staff member is like, what are his standards of sexual behaviour. If the content of the question is answered, the response can hardly be satisfactory because, according to the emotional state of the boy at the time, it may make him feel unreasonably guilty or it may be seen either as a seductive invitation to promiscuity or as 'square' and moralistic. In addition, since a discussion about sexuality with disturbed adolescent boys may be felt by them as exciting, it could also be felt as an unconscious homosexual seduction.

An appropriate response might run as follows: 'You are not sure how you should behave and are trying to make up your mind by finding out what I am like.' Having heard this, the boy may elucidate his own confusion or, if one so wishes and if it is clear that the boy wants it and can accept it, an opinion can be expressed. At the same time the issue of a human need for privacy can be discussed. This same question was in fact asked in an approved school and also by the group in the unit. At an early house meeting, when the question as to how the boys should behave sexually was being discussed, they turned to the psychiatrist and said, 'Did you have intercourse before you married, then?' An interpretation at this point, made in the relationships between the boy and his 'therapist', using the latter word in the broadest sense, is 'expressive', in that it is likely to produce a situation in which a thought that was previously not available to conscious awareness becomes conscious and may be spoken.

Interpretations may also be supportive to the individual in that they help him see the reality of the world around him and what he does to it. A boy in the house infuriated the others by constantly gossiping about them to the staff and subtly letting them know he had done so. He then bitterly complained that they were all antagonistic to him. A supportive comment was that if he did not have some wish to be tormented by the group he would either stop his gossiping or, if he did it, keep quiet about it. Another type of supportive comment will stop a boy from hurting himself. Thus if a boy planned to do something quite destructive, as for example impulsively planning to leave with no plans for the future, one might say, 'The only problem is you cannot run away from yourself, and I will do my best to stop you leaving.' Similarly, on an occasion when the group deteriorated in their behaviour and complained that the house was untidy, the remark was made that they must all have a wish to surround themselves with dirt and they were asked what had happened to their feelings of being worth something as people.

These concepts may, then, be used to describe the type of group therapy used, and a group may be theoretically supportive or expressive, or both. In supportive group therapy the aim is to strengthen the ego of the participants, with a minimum attempt to resolve their unconscious conflicts. In such a therapeutic situation most of the comments of the therapist will be about the way the participants handle their relationship to each other and the outside world. Supportive therapy is to some extent educational and may often be called 'counselling.'

In some situations what passes for counselling is carried on on the assumption that certain topics can appropriately be banned. The value of such procedures, except to make staff feel more valuable and worthwhile, a laudable goal in itself, can be questioned. With individuals suffering from disturbed character problems attending therapeutic groups against their will, 'counselling' in the purely supportive sense is probably worthless. The propensity of delinquent populations to go along with what is expected of them was mentioned in Chapter V. This can apply to 'counselling' situations unless the unexpressed feelings of the groups are understood and appropriately interpreted. These feelings include the individual's sense of being forced into the group situation and his consequent anger with the 'counsellor' and the institution. Ambivalent feelings aroused both by starting with the group and by leaving it also need to be understood and interpreted. Finally, the boys' tendency to use each other to express their anxieties about themselves must be clear in the counsellor's mind and requires interpretation, as do misconceptions about the role of the counsellor.

Expressive group therapy is designed to work primarily with the developing transference neurosis of the participants towards the therapist. Thus interpretations will be made about the unconscious meanings of the patients' words and actions in relation to each other and to the therapist. Other interpretations will show how a relationship with a peer member of the group is unconsciously designed to express feelings about, and attitudes towards, the therapist. This type of therapy in our opinion should take place at least three times weekly and requires the conscious motivation of the participants. It is desirable that they should have personalities able to tolerate internal pain, and their liability to act out their unconscious conflicts on the real world should be minimal.

All types of group interaction designed to help to resolve the emotional difficulties of those attending should properly be called 'group therapy'. The optimum size of a group is nine – eight 'patients' and one therapist. With a skilled therapist it is possible to have more patients, up to twelve as an outside maximum; or fewer, three as a minimum. A group may be 'open', in that when one 'patient' drops out another replaces him, or 'closed', when the group does not replace the fall-outs and thus becomes smaller in size. The life of the group may be determinate, members may agree to meet for a given number of sessions; or indeterminate, in which there is no fixed end-point. Whether the therapy is expressive, supportive, or a mixture of both, a high degree of skill is required on the part of the therapist. It is as inappropriate to assess the results of therapy performed by semi-skilled and semi-trained personnel and to ascribe value to the results as it would be to assess the value of orthopaedic surgery performed by a practitioner who had no special training in that branch of medicine.

In line with its stated goals, the house meeting provided 'supportive-expressive' group therapy. In any one session most of the comments made by the therapist would be supportive, fewer directly interpretative. As the group developed with any one set of boys, ultimately more interpretations and fewer ego-supportive comments would be made.

An example of a mainly supportive session held after a series of episodes in which the boys were stealing from each other follows:

The meeting started in dead silence, and the psychiatrist said 'What's all this about?' This was greeted with monosyllabic replies, 'I didn't say anything', 'He says I've assed about', and finally the psychiatrist commented, 'What is all the feeling going on in the house about?'

First boy: Well, pickpocketing. Not feeling, thieving. I had my 'Brylcreem' whipped and it was locked up. I found it again then (pause).
Psychiatrist: Where did you find it?
First boy: I'm not sure of the name (long pause).

At this point the therapist was acutely aware of the tension between the boys and their obvious anger and fear of expressing it. He decided to make a comment which was designed to be supportive. He made an historical remark with the implication that, since this type of situation had occurred before, it need not be so frightening. He also attempted to correct a misperception.

Psychiatrist: Let me give you a piece of history about stealing in the house. We went through it when the house just opened – through the whole business you are going through now of 'I won't say' and 'I won't tell'. The old borstal business of not shopping on people.
Second boy: Yes, that's perfectly true but you take it the wrong way.
Third boy: I don't know.
First boy: I don't want any trouble.

The next two comments were in a sense of confrontation, 'you are angry with each other', and then a direct support, 'no one will attack anyone else, either by having them thrown into prison or by physical assault'.

Psychiatrist: More trouble will be caused if we play this game of 'not saying'. Trouble and anger with each other, like now.
Third boy: John and I use 'Trugel', sometimes 'Brylcreem' but very seldom. A certain person who has never had it in his life before – we lose two tubes of 'Trugel' – and this person happens to have it in his wardrobe.
Psychiatrist: This is a house where we all live together. No one here is a prison officer with the power to punish and no one hits anyone else.

It is apparent from what follows that the boys now focus the whole problem on an absent boy, who was clearly responsible for many of the thefts, to an extent they were using him as a scapegoat. The psychiatrist felt that the boys were projecting their own guilt and anxiety, since stealing had recently been rampant in the house. He thought that this might be a reaction to the appointment of a new warden, which was shortly followed by the death of her husband. During the course of the group he decided that the most helpful goal would be for the boys to see that the boy on whom the problems of the whole group were focused was not 'bad' but had difficulties with which he might be helped. If they were able to appreciate his situation, to some extent, an attempt to help the boy would be unconsciously perceived as relating to their own difficulties. If this relieved their anxiety the bout of mutual stealing might stop.

Fourth boy: It was Henry's wardrobe, wasn't it?
Second boy: Why didn't you say so?
First boy: I'm frightened of Henry.
Fourth boy: And he took Mac's pound note.
First boy: About a week ago I had had a day off work, Henry took a day off work. Then I went back to work, in the afternoon, it was. I went down into the town and I came back and Henry was in. Rosie was upstairs cleaning Mac's bedroom out, because usually when she's out she locks it, see. She was up there cleaning it out, and on the dressing table I think it was, there was a pound note sticking half out of it, and I had just come in; Rosie came downstairs, Henry was upstairs. Rosie came downstairs and she was talking to me, and it was probably partly my fault, you see, because I held her back; and she was talking about a couple of minutes you see. When she found the pound note had gone she knew that I hadn't got a chance to get nowhere near there, and she told Mrs. D. And she told Mrs. D. that it was impossible for me to have taken it, so she had a chat with Henry about it and got it back. Then on Sunday, Henry he come down and said, 'You've left all your money on your

bed up there, you know he didn't take it from me or anything, he could have picked it up and that was it, he didn't take it from us.

Psychiatrist: Since Henry is not so bad, couldn't you have said something to him about your own loss?

First boy: I don't know whether you'd take offence at that or not, you see. But I know that after that Henry, he definitely would take offence you see. It would upset the bloke if I said anything. I don't know about you so much. That's what I mean.

At this point two boys started to project their difficulties on to the warden in an attempt to alleviate their own anxiety. In his comment, the psychiatrist interpreted this and then went on to point how Henry had fluctuating symptoms.

Third boy: We've got wardrobes upstairs, right?

Fifth boy: The wardrobes are locked, Stan and I have ours locked.

Third boy: Why should Mrs. D. have a key of our wardrobes? Well, I was in there, on Sunday, and the very end key said 'Key to boys' wardrobes'. Why should she have a key to that? It's as bad as borstal. Isn't it?

Psychiatrist: Well, I think you are so fed up about the thieving that the easiest thing to do is to get angry with Mrs. D. for having a key to the wardrobes. Then you don't have to worry about Henry and yourselves.

First boy; Now let me tell you the position as far as Henry is concerned. I think, although I can't prove it, and I have not said this to Henry, that Henry was probably responsible for a lot of the stealing that went on before.

Second boy: (Interruption) Well, that's who I thought was guilty anyway.

Psychiatrist: Then we had months and months and months in which Henry didn't steal anything, neither did anyone else. Now I don't know why all this petty theft has started, but I know it started from the time when Mac lost his pound, because I think there was no stealing before that.

First boy: There wasn't, no.

Psychiatrist: You know, Henry, like everyone else recently, was bothered and upset. Now, the other thing that Mrs. D. did tell me just now, while you all were watching television, was that Henry was very upset because he wouldn't get up this morning.

First Boy: Yeah, he refused to get up.

Psychiatrist: And you know when Henry gets in a state he gets in a state. Now, I don't know what's the matter with Henry and I guess he's run out tonight because he knew this would come up. Perhaps in talking only about Henry we are all running away too. It looks like this. Well, I don't know if you've noticed it or not, but he's obviously very uncomfortable about it, as anybody would be.

Third boy: Because he must know that whoever's 'Trugel' he whipped, he knows John and I have got it back. But he can't find it now because I've hidden it.

It has been emphasized at several points above that boys can accept responsibility for themselves only if they really have it. For disturbed late adolescents, words without an action implication tend to be meaningless. What follows here demonstrated in the group setting the situation in which the boys had to make the decision. It was as if a father said to his son in a family setting, 'I see several alternatives, which would you like me to take?'

Psychiatrist: What we don't want to happen in this house, and I think everybody agrees, is to have the situation as exists in borstal, where people have to hide things to avoid their being stolen. It's a miserable way of living. So we've got a choice, you've all got a choice at this moment in time as to what you do. You all live here and it's up to you.

First boy: Well, I caught him two or three times and I said, 'What are you doing here?' and he said, 'Oh, I'm just looking for a clothes brush.'

Second boy: And I can't prove nothing.

Psychiatrist: I will do what you want me to do. There are three possibilities: either I can tell B.A. or, if you all feel you want me to, I will say to Henry, 'Well, the blokes can't stand it,

145

you've got to find digs.' Alternatively, if you want me to, I can try and talk to him and find out what on earth is the matter that he suddenly starts stealing. This is the choice. When Henry gets upset and bothered, he does several things: one is he steals from people, the second thing he does is he immediately starts to switch jobs, but is it just Henry, doesn't this often happen in the house?

Third boy: He's got another job now, hasn't he.

First boy: Has he? Oh, I didn't know that.

Second boy: Oh, I thought he was in the same job.

Fifth boy: Because he was getting good pay then, wasn't he? He was getting about a pound a week more.

Psychiatrist: The third thing that Henry does is to get very miserable and bad-tempered, and this really goes in waves.

Third boy: Yeah, 'cos he's so bogged up, because I know him, as you say.

First boy: Well, yes.

Second boy: Poor old Henry.

Third boy: Well, old Henry thinks he can take things, yet he's got money on him.

Second boy: It's pointless, he could easily go and buy these little things.

Fifth boy: I know he's never used them. I've been here four months now, and I've never once seen him use them.

Third boy: He doesn't do it just 'cos he wants the stuff, it's 'cos there's something wrong with him.

Psychiatrist: Some people when they get upset get bellyache, some get drunk, some people steal in a crazy way. Now, what I want to know from you blokes is whether we are going to try to help him sort himself out and have him stay here, or you can have him thrown out.

Third boy: Well I don't like the idea of him getting chucked out, he's not so different from anyone else, is he?

The group finally concluded this topic by saying that they wanted Henry to admit to them all that he had taken the goods and run the risk that whatever else was stolen he might be blamed. They were able to face the implication of his misery, and started then to talk more of their own experiences of theft and what it meant and how punishment didn't seem to stop them in itself. In fact, following a series of largely supportive and non-interpretative comments from the doctor, the group talked of feeling and not thieving, although their intention was quite the opposite. One comment made in the nature of an interpretation led to the group becoming less defensive; 'No one here is a prison officer' meant to the boys 'You will not be persecuted'.

Following this meeting the thieving stopped. Henry came to the house meeting the next week, and to his astonishment the boys were helpful and not overtly critical. Nevertheless this did not resolve the group's inclination to use him as a scapegoat for their own difficulties, nor his provocation of this. When he became involved in a similar situation two months later, much the same process had to be gone through again, but the boys were more insightful.

It would appear that supportive therapy alone, with boys such as these, cannot help them to overcome their feelings of persecution by the outside world; a helpful comment at a superficial level is inadequate. If, in the above example, the therapy had been largely expressive, the initial silence might have been interpreted quite differently, but capacity for direct verbal communication was, we think, enhanced by the technique used here. The discomfort most consciously felt by the boys was whether or not they could talk of the thefts. It was believed that it was most important that the boys feel able to verbalize this safely. The boys who commented about Mrs. D. having the key to their wardrobes both felt women as an emotional threat to their masculine status. An interpretative comment about this was possible, but would have created an entirely different therapeutic atmosphere. The fact that Mrs. D.'s husband had just died and she had survived has been mentioned as possibly having relevance. If this issue had been brought up by the psychiatrist – assuming this to be an accurate understanding of the situation – the degree of anxiety experienced by the boys might have been intolerable, so that either they would have had to deny the validity of the interpretation, not a directly destructive response, or they might have acted out the conflict in an even more self-destructive manner.

The therapeutic groups in the house from its inception seemed to fall into a series each with its own life-cycle. Although the groups were open, the tendency was for a number of boys to leave at the same time, leaving a residual small group of four or five. The sequence was as follows. When a boy first came to the house he tended for the first few weeks to be relatively silent in the group. When he became more integrated, it would appear that the group often reacted to the emotional threat of his participation by being aggressive with each other: on some occasions, in terms of noisy behaviour; on others, in terms of material thefts from each other. When the disturbance subsided the hostility would tend to be focused by the group on the resident staff, sometimes in words, sometimes in deeds. At this point it became possible directly to focus hostility on the therapist in the group. When this happened the house became a relatively easy place in which to live, and at about that time some boys would leave to live in the community at large. The length of the cycle varied according to several determinants. It became shorter as the psychiatrist and staff became more experienced; it tended to lengthen if a number of new boys came in within a short time of each other. If the outside stresses were great, as, for example, when there was a recession and a good deal of local unemployment, the boys tended to become more aggressive with each other and the staff. If any boy fell foul of the law for any reason this clearly was depressing to the group at large, as a previous example (see p. 101) has shown. The onset of holiday periods for the staff interrupted the cycle and would lead to restless and disturbed behaviour, in which many boys would move around the room and find excuses to leave early or to miss the session altogether. An example of a session in which the boys focused their anger on the psychiatrist and then on each other, and then became constructive, is as follows:

Therapeutic Techniques: The group process

There were six boys present, the total number living in the house at the time. Another boy who was shortly to leave had his young brother staying in the house, but he was not present at the meeting. The setting in which the meeting took place was unusual in that the normal room was out of commission owing to redecoration. The background situation was one in which a series of aggressive actions towards the assistant warden had taken place. Boys had borrowed his clothes – shirts and sweaters – without permission, and two days prior to the meeting two of them had pushed his car backwards down the drive so that the back wheels were in the road. A policeman had seen this and charged them with 'taking a car without the owner's permission'. The magistrate had dismissed the case.

The psychiatrist had cancelled the previous week's house meeting and was a few minutes late for the session to be reported upon. The boys were obviously agitated and kept asking the warden when the psychiatrist was going to turn up.

The boys sat down and one of them rather truculently said, 'What do you want to talk to us about, then?' Another boy asked for permission to leave because he was decorating the other room. Being refused, he burst into an angry tirade about how the psychiatrist would be responsible if the decorations were not done. 'The trustees can pay for them and it will bloody well be your fault.' The outburst was ignored, and the boys persisted in asking what the psychiatrist wanted to talk about. The question was turned back to them, and a blast of anger came from the group. They announced that they were forced to come; that in any case the psychiatrist didn't think it important because he had missed the previous week; and it was no use because nobody said anything, anyway. The psychiatrist commented that this was up to them. They then talked of the car episode, expressing glee at what they imagined the magistrate to have said and contempt for the policeman who they thought had been lying and caught out. They said that there was nothing wrong in moving the car because the law said they were 'not guilty'. The interpretative comment was made that they were now being like the 'lying

149

police', because they knew perfectly well that their fiddling about with Mac's car was a nasty inconsiderate thing to do, the same sort of action as taking his shirts.

There was a flurry from two boys that 'Mac takes it as a joke, he doesn't mind', which other boys contradicted as a matter of fact. At this point the psychiatrist said that these actions took place because they were so envious and jealous of Mac, Mrs. D., and him himself; that they felt helpless about this, and their behaviour was a way of showing us all how they felt. Thereupon, the whole tone of the meeting changed, and they began to talk of how 'Mac is much better than us, in a different class'. They expressed a 'we–they' feeling, with themselves as the inferior 'we'. The psychiatrist said that they were also talking about him, and one of the boys said pathetically, 'You've got a family, a big house, and a car. You had all the chances, we've had none. You must be better than we are.' There was much talk about this, and finally the psychiatrist commented that they used this feeling to justify their own angry behaviour and sometimes they didn't just try to take it out on the staff but also out on each other. 'That's right, somebody was in my wardrobe the other day; I know who it is but I'm not going to say.' A boy came back with, 'Yes, it was me, and you gave me permission.' They elucidated this, and it finally emerged that the boy's brother had gone into his wardrobe. They then talked very freely of how they had taken things from each other, each admitting his own role. The interpretation was then made that they took things from each other because they felt all the time that one was getting more than the other, not just of things but also of affection and care. At this point they discussed their relationship with Mrs. D. and Mac, their competitiveness with each other, their feelings that if a boy spent time with Mrs. D. he was inevitably trying to get others into trouble. The tension of the meeting had considerably subsided, and one boy said, 'Things are much better if we talk to each other.' The psychiatrist commented that they had asked him what the meeting was for, surely they had found the answer themselves.

There were occasions, it would seem, when the house meeting

demonstrated the similarity of feeling towards a particular boy on the part of the rest of the boys and the staff. When this occurred it was sometimes possible to dovetail the situation in a helpful way. As we have mentioned, a problem often perceived by the staff was the demanding greed of a boy. If it persisted it was likely to arouse in the staff angry feelings of rejection, which were themselves likely to make him more clinging and demanding. At the same time as this feeling was active between the staff and the boy, the other boys would be expressing anger and hostility towards him because he got so much attention.

A boy on one occasion expressed the feeling to the psychiatrist in an individual meeting that 'Mrs. D. prefers everyone else to me.' The latter then realized that, in every meeting he had with the staff, discussions about this one boy took up more than half the time.

It was as if, from time to time, one boy became the focus for the anxiety of the whole house. Not only would this happen over this type of attention-getting, it also occurred from time to time if a boy persistently stole, particularly when the stealing was associated very clearly with the boy's feeling rejected. The realization by the staff that such boys were in fact getting too much attention of an unhelpful kind, that is of wary and angry involvement, and in a subtle way they were not getting the positive attention and care that the other boys were receiving, was always helpful.

An early problem, in terms of the development of the house, concerned who should attend house meetings other than the boys and the psychiatrist. It was a particularly vital issue because non-participant staff sometimes appeared to feel that the meeting was an esoteric affair conducted out of the psychiatrist's unconscious.

At a discussion with the rest of the team the psychiatrist casually mentioned that it was clear that the boys fantasied that the assistant warden had a sexual relationship with the warden, and were jealous about it. This statement was greeted with what appeared to be frank disbelief.

When much later in a temper a boy made exactly the same remark to the warden, it was less of a shock than it otherwise would have been.

In the early years of the project the house meeting was sometimes used by some members of the team to criticize the working of the whole house. When the boys were being particularly infantile, which aroused considerable concern, the suggestion would perhaps be made that the house meeting could be used to persuade them to do some good work for others. This was part of an implication that was being passed to the resident staff that in some way they could make the boys unselfish people. At such times the resident staff might be asked whether they thought the house meeting was of any use. This was a very reasonable question, but one that was asked, we felt, more with the expectation of a negative than a positive reply.

A conception that was held about the house meeting prior to the opening of Northways was that it would be a 'family night' in which the staff, the boys, and the psychiatrist should meet together to discuss problems, plan projects, and so on. This was an image which in fact never materialized in this way. It was based on an understandable misapprehension as to the degree of inner disturbance and ego weakness from which the boys suffered.

When the house first opened the warden and his wife attended some of the original house meetings. Unfortunately they were rapidly used by the boys, who were at that time particularly anxious in the new situation, as a focus for their projected image of bad, depriving parents. To be able to tolerate this degree of hostility, not react to it in a controlling way, and then have an authority role on the strength of one's relationship with the boys, required a degree of skill that it was unreasonable to expect from a couple who had little in the way of formal training. Experience alone is not enough. The situation was such that if a potentially important authority figure, the warden, could be attacked, successfully in the boys' eyes, in a group setting, it would become difficult for them to see him as a worthwhile identification figure. Skill and training of a high degree were needed to ensure that the attack was not seen as successful. Merely applying superego pressure would, it was felt, resolve nothing in the long run for the individual boy. Because of this the house meetings normally included only the boys and the psychiatrist, a system that was continued throughout the project. After each house meeting the psychiatrist would meet the resident staff to give them a very general run-down of the situation as it appeared in the group at the time. After the house had settled down, at no time did the staff feel the boys had successfully manipulated the psychiatrist against them and vice versa. Once the boys knew that neither the resident staff nor the psychiatrist was susceptible to manipulation they ceased these efforts, which were not a problem after the first six months of the existence of the house. One advantage of not having resident staff at the house meetings was that the boys were able to use words more freely. This was not so much because of the staff's need to have socially acceptable words used, but because boys would feel that if they could use socially inappropriate language to the staff in one situation, they could freely do so in another.

To the mature adult, words are a highly meaningful communication device which normally have more significance than non-verbal communication. To the disturbed adolescent, the reverse is often true: actions may speak more loudly and meaningfully than words. Often such an individual will tell an adult of his antisocial behaviour, or behave with him in an antisocial way, in an unconscious attempt to corrupt the adult and have him collude in this behaviour. If this unconscious attempt to destroy the adult as a worthwhile person succeeds, he then ceases to be a satisfactory identification figure, and attempts at therapeutic help will fail. In Northways a situation such as this often arose. The staff had never to be in a situation in which they would appear to be agreeing by inaction that unacceptable behaviour was acceptable. This has been illustrated above in connection with the issues of aggressive behaviour (p. 17) and inappropriate sexual activity (p. 125); it could also be important in terms of what a boy might be allowed to say, for example:

On the occasion when a boy angrily told the warden that she didn't want him around because she was having sexual relations with her assistant and his presence would interfere, she reacted with horror and shock, asked him how he dared say such a thing, and told him to leave the room.

This was an entirely appropriate and helpful response. It provided a control for the boy, and demonstrated that she was not going to allow him verbally to corrupt her. Although her reaction did not stop the boy from being tormented by such a feeling, it conveyed that it could not appropriately be stated in words to her. To some degree, both in the group situation and in individual relationships, the psychiatrist could be non-judgemental about such a feeling, and so make its resolution possible. Nevertheless, he had implicitly to convey that this was a socially unacceptable concept. In the group the issue of collusion was also relevant:

> Two boys boasted in a house meeting that they had property which was not their own and to which they had no right. This put the psychiatrist in a dilemma. If, on the one hand, he told the authorities, he was breaking his word to the boys that he would keep their confidences; on the other, whatever interpretation or comment he might make, if he did nothing he was passively agreeing that the act was acceptable. This was interpreted to the boys; the psychiatrist said that he could not go along with an illegal act, and the goods were returned to the owner.

If the boys had not been willing to do this they would then have had to leave the house. The reason for this is that if the psychiatrist was successfully corrupted in the eyes of the group, he would have ceased to be a worthwhile figure with whom they might identify. The situation did not come to this in fact, but if it had, this would have been conveyed to the group.

CHAPTER X

Therapeutic Techniques

The social system and the socialization of the boys

THE DEVELOPMENT OF THE SOCIAL SYSTEM

IN EARLIER chapters we have sketched out the sociotherapeutic environment that was to be created, but this developed slowly and many errors were made. It took some time before role definition became clear, and in the early days of the project it appeared to the boys that there was a plethora of potential authority figures, some of whom clearly had real power over the boys, others of whom did not.

The boys knew that the trustee body existed, but were unclear about its functions, except that it had provided the funds for the house. The boys had some feeling that 'he who pays the piper, calls the tune'. The Director of the Borstal Division and his staff were felt to be waiting in the wings to recall the boys at the slightest provocation; this was felt as an anxiety but was perhaps a wish. The warden's role was quite unclear to the boys. This title, as has been said, was not used by the boys. The warden was put rather in the position of someone who would inevitably spend time passing on information to the Borstal Division, who would certainly use it against them. They saw the psychiatrist in the traditional image of a 'nut doctor', a little mad himself. They felt that he would be interested in proving that they themselves were mad; he was certainly not to be believed, and they were most anxious about his function.

Since we opened the house with three boys and we were all over-anxious, staff and boys alike, it was as if too many staff were chasing too few boys. This meant that from time to time a boy could play the typical institutional game of divide and rule. Eventually, roles became more clearly differentiated, as we have described. Borstal After-Care relatively withdrew from the day-to-day running of the house, although when the first warden left the boys used the director, the supervising officer, and the psychiatrist as vital sheet-anchors.

Again, the first group of boys were plunged into a model of a 'home' situation which had not yet gained any social stability. They had not had the experience of a code of family living inside themselves. They dealt with their anxiety by shrewdly testing the limits, assessing the risks, and seeing how far they could go. Ultimately the warden's and the psychiatrist's authority became clear to the boys and they knew exactly the extent to which we would use it in action.

The only real authority was to ask a boy to leave. Apart from a decision that we felt a boy was ready to live away from the house, in two and a half years, out of twenty-one boys, this was done at short notice with only two boys; one for hitting another boy and one for having a girl sleep in the house. Two of the boys who were about ready to leave demonstrated this by failing to pay their rent. There was considerable discussion with them about this over several weeks and finally they moved out two weeks in arrears, the period we had set with them as the maximum of latitude in this area.

It took some time for the resident staff to learn not to be over-anxious about the boys. Although the boys might subtly demand 'mothering', they did not want a mother or father, and if we were not over-concerned about their bed-time, whether they locked up or not, whether or not they came to meals, there was less trouble in these areas.

If the warden pressed the issue of the boys saving money they were less likely to do it than if she did not. If they brought a girl-friend of doubtful value to the house a raised eyebrow was more effective than a long comment. In short, when a stable background to their lives was provided the boys functioned better when their adolescent negativism was not aroused. This did not mean over-permissiveness; it meant an absence of fuss.

An effective way of reviewing the development of the house is to look at the history of the house meetings, which mirrored the creation of the social system.

The house first opened when it was physically incomplete and was still being decorated by boys from one of the borstal institutions, who chose the first scheme of decorations. The small North-ways group talked of expressing their gratitude to them by giving them a small party when they had finished. However, they used the opportunity of one of these boys stealing from the house and absconding with his loot not to do so.

In the first stages of the house meetings, attendance was quite voluntary, and no implication was conveyed to the boys that if they did not attend we would take it that they wished to leave. At first, reacting in a manner typical of deprived children, they were only too willing to talk to someone providing they were given a chance. Initially, therefore, there was no difficulty about attendance at house meetings. After several weeks it became clear that willingness to attend depended on three factors: the meetings had to be seen by the boys as giving them something specific, providing money or material things; no topic must be discussed that would make them anxious; and the psychiatrist could not cancel a meeting for any reason. If he did, they denied any feeling about the cancellation but for one reason or another one or two of them would fail to appear themselves at the next meeting or be very late.

The first two of these determinants were unclear to us before the event and were not predicted. Before the first boys came to the unit, we knew of the inadequacy of the physical resources with which they would leave borstal institutions, in particular a shortage of clothing and money. Because of this, the psychiatrist wrote the following formal note to the trustees eight days before the house opened.

'Most boys leave borstal, as you know, with very little in the way of funds. I feel we should set up some sort of central borrowing fund which the boys might administer themselves with assistance from the staff.'

On discussion, it also seemed that this might help to prevent them from buying goods on credit, thus maintaining their false illusions about the real value of goods. A loan fund of £50 was therefore created, the idea being that as boys repaid their loans to it, others could borrow. In fact, we were unwittingly creating a situation in which we were colluding with the boys' wish to gain immediate gratification. For the first weeks the house meetings were seen by the boys as being like a fountain from which, if they behaved appropriately, real blessings might flow. It soon became apparent that the boys were able to perceive their own needs and not the needs of others, and the first four boys rapidly used up the credit. They paid lip-service to the idea of repayment before the next boy arrived. In fact, when he came, he had some thirty shillings available to him. In addition, the warden was put in the position of being the person who was a 'real' withholder, the repayments were to be collected with the boys' 'rent'. On the other hand, the psychiatrist was a 'real' giver, in that it was from the house meetings that approval was given for a boy to receive the money. Thus unconsciously we also perpetuated the boys' inclination to split their perception of people into 'good' and 'bad'.

Although a boy might talk of coming to the house meetings to help sort out either his own difficulties or difficulties in the house; a more valid reason would be that he wished to get money for some new clothes. He would be anxious in case a non-appearance on his own part might mean that another boy would get what he considered to be his due. The institutional system, in which the boys were giving us the words they thought we wanted, but were actually using the social system to obtain immediate gratification, was thus perpetuated. The loan fund was used by the boys as a cover to avoid facing their real difficulties. After four months the whole idea was dropped, and we attempted to collect back as much as we could, in the house meeting and through the supervising officer, to repay the trustees.

The only advantage of the loan fund arrangement was that the first group of boys did not buy goods on the hire-purchase system, and it was two years before a boy did this. Then he was so aware of its unacceptability in the house that he mentioned it only after the event. There was a small flurry in which one of the boys got himself appointed as an agent to a mail-order house (which sent goods with no references). This led to such chaos among a small sub-group of the boys that the idea was rapidly dropped. A further bar to hire-purchase agreements was that the boys were mostly not of legal age to enter into such commitments, although this does not appear to be effective with some firms.

The house was initially incompletely furnished, and this again led to a situation in which the meeting was seen as being important for what the group could obtain. The meeting might discuss the need for a television set or a record-player or ornaments for one of the rooms. If the demand seemed reasonable the psychiatrist would ask the trustees to provide the items, which they invariably did. On the one hand, this had the advantage that it gave the boys a stake in choosing some of the furniture of the house; on the other, it helped to perpetuate in the boys' minds a false image of the reason for the house meetings. In addition this tended to put the trustees in a position in which they were seen by the boys as the all-too-willing providers, who gave goods to the boys without their having to put in more effort than attending the house meeting.

Since the boys were unable to provide any service of any worth or significance to the house or to the community at the time – it was winter and they all had to establish themselves in jobs – it would probably have been better if the house had been completed before they moved in.

If Northways had been a boys' club it would have been desirable for a great deal to have been left to the boys to do themselves in terms of really providing or building what was necessary. Since it was a home this was probably inappropriate. Nevertheless, we unconsciously infantilized the boys who were in any case highly unstable and immature, by asking them what they would like, without expecting them to put any real effort, either financial or otherwise, into getting it.

An unfortunate effect of these errors was that we found ourselves creating a social system in which the warden's authority was grossly undermined. The head of a household should, after all, decide on the furniture. Not surprisingly, the warden reacted with frustration, and in many ways was felt by the boys to be unreasonable with them. In so far as this was true, the psychiatrist then found himself in the position in which the boys had real and valid complaints. They provoked this type of situation as much as possible, unconsciously if not consciously, and the house meeting began to act as an emotional support against what the boys perceived as a thoroughly bad external world – the warden and his wife. If they attended the house meeting the boys verbally attacked them, if they failed to attend the attack still persisted. An example of this is as follows:

We had agreed, staff and boys alike, that the kitchens would be left open so that the boys could get snacks if they so wished. The warden complained to the boys that they were making too much noise turning the fluorescent light on and off (the kitchen was directly below his bedroom). They responded by becoming more noisy, so the warden locked the kitchen door. The boys then provocatively made as much noise as they could. They came to the house meeting and bitterly complained that the warden was being punitive and unreasonable. He had said to the psychiatrist, 'I decided I would teach them a lesson.' If the kitchen was re-opened his authority was undermined, if it was not the whole concept of the sort of house we wished to run would be destroyed. The psychiatrist also found himself in the position of having to use his verbal authority to get the boys to stop their provocative attacks. Thus, by protecting the warden, who felt the situation was out of hand, he colluded in the boys' concept that he was a weak and inadequate man.

With these factors at work during the first months of the project, attendance at the house meeting tended to be very good and, there appeared no reason for making it compulsory. However gradually it became clear to the psychiatrist what was really happening.

After the loan-fund project was cancelled, the psychiatrist began to interpret to the boys their provocative manipulation; at this point the general atmosphere of the house relaxed, but the house meeting became less comfortable for the boys and the level of potential anxiety was raised. During the initial months, as has been mentioned, when the psychiatrist had to miss the occasional house meeting, one or two boys were late on subsequent occasions, though they denied that they minded the cancellation. They now took the opportunity not to appear at all, and attendances began to fall off dramatically; at one meeting no boys arrived. The psychiatrist reacted to this by interpreting the boys' contempt for him, telling them they could feel this but not act upon it, and made attendance at the house meetings obligatory. The boys who lived in the house at that time were told that if they failed to come he would take it that they felt ready to live in the community at large. They became openly angry but attended regularly.

At about this time the warden resigned, and for several months a number of housemasters from borstal were temporarily seconded to the house, various supervising officers acting as their reliefs when they were off duty. One might have expected a great deal of disturbed behaviour as a result, particularly as this was a period of great instability in the house owing to uncertainty about the time any one housemaster or supervising officer would be able to stay. In fact, the house ran fairly smoothly for several reasons. The staff seconded to the house were able and sensitive and found the whole experience worthwhile. They also brought with them an authority status, which meant that the boys were likely to react, as they had in borstal, with a tendency to compliance. The psychiatrist's role, both in the meetings and in the house generally, changed.

On the one hand, the psychiatrist took a more expressive course in the house meetings, on the other, he became much more directly involved in the day-to-day running of the house. When there was no staff able to stay, he slept there. The boys also visited him at his home from time to time. Ostensibly this was to do odd jobs such as gardening, concrete-laying, and car-washing to earn some money. In fact, it allowed them the chance to spend time in a one-to-one relationship with a stable figure who was not leaving and to experience something of a family background. All the boys did this in an informal rotation, and arrangements would be made at the house meeting the week before. The Director of Borstal After-Care also became more directly involved with the boys by coming to dinner, asking the occasional boy to his home, and discussing with them many aspects of living in a highly informal way. The very reality of this type of involvement implicitly dealt with the boys' hyper-suspiciousness towards him. When they met him so frequently it was difficult for them to perceive him as a hostile figure lying in wait to pounce on them for the slightest misdemeanour.

Clearly there were disadvantages in presenting the boys with the reality of a family group to which they could not belong. Although it is true that this might lead to feelings of envy and jealousy which the boys would have to tolerate, at a time of crisis in the unit, when they felt deprived of a stable central figure, it was also perceived by them as a very real 'caring for' gesture. In that they did not become overtly disturbed, the results showed that the latter quality outweighed the former. Since we knew that no one temporary warden would be able to stay for very long, this protected the boys from becoming highly involved with them and so made it easier for them to tolerate the inevitable chopping and changing. One effect of all this was to create a situation in which the boys felt a conscious need to be present at the house meeting, which, once again, was giving them a degree of emotional support which their day-to-day lives tended at that time not to be able to provide. It was only when there was once again stability in the house that the meetings began to be seen by the boys as a source of anxiety rather than as a way of alleviating it.

When told of the warden's resignation, the boys became extremely anxious in the group. Suddenly they began to feel that the warden and his wife were really very good people. They felt that the resignation was a result of their bad behaviour and they became very guilty. No attempt was made to alleviate this feeling by denying their responsibility to them; rather it was worked with in the light of their past experiences of loss, particularly their separation from their real parents.

Comparable guilt with less immediate reality to it was to emerge at a much later date; when a new warden died the boys again reacted as if they had a personal responsibility. On this occasion, the boys were helped to see how they felt responsible because of their own past experiences and the present situation in which, from time to time, they had felt angry and critical of him, and the reality of the situation was also firmly conveyed to them.

The initial errors in distorting the social system have been described, but there were certain assets to the situation. Voluntary attendance at group meetings, with no implication that non-attendance meant that they might wish to leave, helped to create in the boys' minds some feeling of real responsibility for what was going on in the house. Although the boys were being seduced, either by what we were doing or by outside pressures, into wanting to come to the house meetings, consciously they felt that they had made a free decision. At a time when there was no social stability built into the house, this enhanced in the individual boy a wish to be constructive.

The first boys who came to the house were told very definitively of the importance of the project as providing a model for future homes for boys with similar difficulties to their own. It was pointed out to them that if support for such projects was to be obtained society was entitled to feel that they would be successful. In the consideration of Northways as a model community this was a special factor which probably could not be repeated. Our use of it, in this way, helped reinforce the constructive wishes of the boys at a time of particular stress for them and for the staff. After the first month or two this issue was no longer raised.

Over the first year of the project the house meetings had an important role in building a conception of decent behaviour into the social system. This process was helped by the fact that the Director of Borstal After-Care sat in on the occasional meeting when the house was first opened. He did not participate in actually working out any concept but his presence gave implicit approval to the value of what the boys were doing in the meetings. He was an authority figure, as has been said, who was endowed by the boys with rather magical powers. The fact that he attended some meetings meant that anything that was evolved about important behavioural social issues was more likely to be meaningful.

If the boys were not to be presented with a set of written rules when they came to the unit, a mass of decisions needed to be made, in particular the social system's attitudes towards visitors of both sexes, sexual activity, aggressive behaviour, times of coming in, and responsibility for the property. Concepts of sharing and of caring about one's fellows were also highly significant for the development of the house. Above all, it was important that the group should not set up a covert social system of their own unknown to the staff.

As far as visitors were concerned, the concepts of the house meeting and the home model were reinforced by the attitudes of the staff towards the boys. They were told that just as no one visits a home to look it over to see how a family functions, no one would visit the unit with such intentions. No one would be brought to visit the house by any of the staff or by members of Borstal After-Care without the boys' foreknowledge and approval. The attitudes of the boys towards bringing people from outside the house to visit were worked out over the first few weeks. With the very rare individual exception, the boys kept to these throughout the period under review. For example:

The first group of boys spent a house meeting discussing the fantasy that they would hold alcoholic parties for people of both sexes. They talked of the need for barrels of beer and it was clear that sexual activity would be the norm.

This was not unlike the fantasy that many adolescents in an equivalent situation might have had. The idea was nevertheless taken seriously, and discussed at length over several meetings. The psychiatrist deliberately played for time. He made it clear that neither he nor the warden had the authority to arrange such a party. There were no funds for the beer, and it was possible that the trustees would object. They were, however, told that if they really wanted such a party they could ask the trustees. The group finally decided that such a party would be difficult to run and might make a mess of the house. A parallel discussion was held over the problem of girl-friends visiting the house. They had to consider the implications of any plan they might put forward and take the ultimate responsibility for it. They finally concluded that girl visitors should be out by approximately 11.0 p.m. They agreed that they ought to take their girl-friends home, and the public transport system was such that if they left later than this they would have to walk back home.

The issue of sexual behaviour was a live one for the group. At first, as has been said, the boys tried to get the staff to tell them what they should do. The boys were told of our attitude towards promiscuous sexual behaviour: that it was loveless, initially maybe exciting, but ultimately likely to become as boring as masturbation. If they wanted to be promiscuous, we in fact could not stop them. The boys finally decided that they should not, whatever the individual's moral values were, have sexual intercourse in the house. They also decided that girls should not go upstairs to the bedrooms. Through the project we knew of two situations in which boys departed from this standard.

As far as male visitors were concerned, the boys decided that they did not want the house to become the hang-out for local delinquents. To some extent they reached this conclusion because of their anxiety about being robbed. This certainly represented their unconscious fear of being plundered of the few good objects in their inner world. It translated in reality to the conclusion that strangers should not be allowed on the bedroom floor unless they had been specifically invited to spend the night in the spare room.

They decided that they ought to ask the warden before a male visitor spent the night and if they brought friends into the house they should not disturb the other boys. Occasionally they were excessively noisy, but this was never a major problem. From time to time they had their friends sleep on the floor of the living-room if they had invited them back after a party or dance, but this was never a cause for real concern. On such occasions the warden would, if it was appropriate, express the disapproval of a reasonable parent figure, either that they hadn't told her – 'How could we? You were asleep' – or that they had left a mess behind. This disapproval was given with the recognition to ourselves that in general this was a harmless thing for them to do. In fact we were giving the boys an area of licensed rebellion. They thought we disapproved, we helped to perpetuate this idea, but we knew they had to assert themselves rebelliously on occasion. The occasional boy brought home a friend whom we knew to have been in trouble with the law, but mostly these friendships, when they did occur, would be out of the house. Nevertheless, they were discussed in the house meeting; in particular there was an occasion when a highly disturbed boy became friendly with a known fence.

As can be seen, what was being worked out was the model of a home situation. Thus, for example, the boys ultimately agreed that it was quite reasonable to bring a friend in for tea or coffee and biscuits in the evening, which they might make themselves; if someone was to come for a meal they would ask. Once this was agreed in the house group, it did not need to be formally restated. If the occasional boy brought someone in at short notice, provided food was available they would be fed. This was less of a problem than it might have been with a group of more mature boys, as, in general, the group found it so difficult to share 'good' things that they could not comfortably bring others into the house to share their food.

Partly because of their mixed feelings about their own inner security, it took many months before a firm conclusion could be reached about coming in at night. They agreed that if they stayed out all night they ought to let the warden know in advance. This was put forward by the psychiatrist to the group as a suggestion. At first they reacted with the strong feeling that this would mean they were being babied. As they began to feel what they did mattered to the warden, who cared about their fate, and as they felt no longer spied upon, impulsive staying-out considerably decreased. Times at which they would return to the house in the evening were more complicated to evolve. The issue revolved around the locking of the front and back doors of the house. This was an intermittent preoccupation of the boys in the house meetings. Initially we were doubtful about their having keys, and the boys felt that they could not as individuals be trusted with a key, because someone would certainly lose one and 'anyone could then come in'. They tried a system in which one boy would stay up to let the last latecomer in at twelve midnight. This did not work, because the boy would go to bed or the time of arrival would be much later than they envisaged. Then the boy would climb through a window and once again the boys became anxious about the security of the house. They then conceived of a situation in which the front-door key would be attached by a string to the letter-box and one had only to reach inside to get it. The boys would tend to leave the key hanging outside, and once again they became concerned. Long before they came to the point of wanting to, the staff felt that they could each have keys and it was indicated to them again and again that they could have a key each if they so wished. It was months after this that the group was able to say that they each wanted a key.

Repeatedly in this study the point has been made that adolescents should have the amount of responsibility with which they are able to deal. The time taken by the group to come to a decision as to whether they should be free to come and go as they liked is a measure of their insecurity and uncertainty as to how much freedom they could handle.

At about the same time as the group felt able to take the responsibility for saying that they could look after the house and have a door key each, the anxiety level in the group again rose. In other words they were continuing a process in which their disturbed behaviour was less likely to appear in society at large and in the house; it was more likely to be present in the group situation. Compared with the traditional psychotherapeutic model, their disturbance was now in the transference situation in the group meeting, which tended to be attended reluctantly thenceforth. This is precisely the situation that occurs in expressive psychotherapy. Just as that cannot contain all the acting-out of potential conflicts, which get spilled over into society, the same occurred with the house group. Thus when episodes of upset behaviour did occur, they could be looked upon as the inevitable failure of the formal group process to contain them. Since, as has been said, the group meetings took place only once weekly and normally lasted one and a half hours, this was partly a function of time, partly that there had to be occasions when the group was not sufficiently supportive, on others it might not be expressive enough. To put this in the most simple terms, if a boy was able to understand his conflictual feelings in a given situation in the house meeting, and his internal emotional balance was not over-disturbed, he was less likely to act out his feelings in the house. If he acted out his conflicts by disturbed behaviour in the group, to a lesser extent the same applied. The inevitability of such behaviour did not mean that it was either approved of, or colluded in, by the staff or the psychiatrist. On occasions when a house meeting was helpful, the resident staff would report a distinct easing of tension in the house; an unhelpful meeting would not have this effect and might enhance tension.

There were occasions in which it became clear through the house meetings that an area of permissiveness was more than the boys could handle. There are two examples of this which are pertinent. In the first instance, as has been mentioned, the boys were given too much latitude over the payment of their rent. There was an explicit expectation that they would pay, but if they were in financial difficulties they were allowed to defer payment of some part or all. This led to many tensions among the boys; those who were paying resented the fact that others did not. To some boys this permissiveness represented an area of living which they could over-easily manipulate. With much overt anxiety, they became so deeply in debt to the house that they could not possibly pay in a reasonable period of time. This became clear to the staff and also was evident by the tension in the house meetings over money. At this point the sliding-scale already discussed was instituted. Failure to pay their fair share of running the house was taken as a message by which the boys would indicate their wish to leave.

A boy was in many ways difficult in his relationship with the warden, which he finally contained, but he then began to get behind in his payments of rent. She said to him 'If you are difficult to live with, we can work it out, I can forgive you and we can get over it; if you don't pay the rent you make me powerless and inevitably the trustees will assume that you do not wish to stay.'

Another area in which without help the boys could not contain their greed was with food. Initially we left the kitchen, the refrigerator, and the food store open. The boys discovered that they were eating each other's breakfasts, and snacks available for all the group would be consumed by one or two boys. From time to time, when they were quite comfortable, the boys could manage not to do this to each other, but whenever they were under stress, with girl-friends, money, or jobs, this greed for food would return. It was as if they gorged and then deprived themselves. For this reason a system was eventually devised by which food was left out in the kitchen and refrigerator for snacks. If this ran out the boys could ask the warden for the key to the storeroom, which was kept in her flat. This was not refused when asked for, but the mere process of having to ask acted as a control.

A preoccupation of the house meetings throughout the whole history of the house was the issue of consideration for the feelings of others. The boys were all severely disturbed, and to achieve a modification of their ego attitudes to include an ability to care for others would represent an adaptation to society at a better level. In a minimal way they had this capacity, as was demonstrated by our being able to get them to consider other boys in a similar position to themselves for a short period of time. We tended to believe prior to opening the unit that with their division of the world into 'we' and 'they' they would care for each other. It was possible that this concern might be very tenuous and depend on the given boy conforming to the mores of the group, but somewhat naïvely we expected a degree of group cohesion. Our population did not show this quality. From time to time, if they all experienced the same external pressure and shared a common emotional problem, they showed a pseudo-cohesion, for example, if they had the feeling they had been unjustly treated by society. Nevertheless, at times such as these the boys were also being aggressive to each other in many ways; competing for attention and robbing each other of small but emotionally precious articles. When this came up in the house group the boys' first response was invariably an attitude that this was happening but one must on no account say whom one suspected. Beneath this pseudo-loyalty was a fear of reprisal. When this was understood and in the open in the group the boys would usually name the person they suspected. This would be followed by a period of mutual projection; the other boy was 'bad' and should be thrown out. When they understood something of the motives behind any episode of theft, they would then begin to demonstrate a wish to help and were capable of some insight. They began to see how they attacked each other when they were worried and anxious. At such times they could openly admit their own part in a theft. As has already been said, part of the problem was their highly mixed feeling towards possessions and their inability to keep a sense of value over things. There appeared to be little difference in their attitude towards stealing from each other and stealing from the outside world, except that they saw the former as safe. To the staff, however, the two forms of theft were seen in quite a

Therapeutic Techniques: The social system and socialization

different light; as we have said, if a boy stole from society at large we had to act and could not 'just talk' about it and try to contain it in our relationship with the boys.

Society tends not to make this differentiation. For example, boys are still sent to approved schools for stealing only from their parents, although this is almost always a sign of intrafamilial disturbance. It is, of course, an antisocial act, but no more antisocial than failing an examination which one has the ability to pass, as an aggressive act directed towards one's family.

It seemed that the boys' stealing from each other was partly related to institutional behaviour, particularly when they first came to the house. Partly it represented their technique of aggressive behaviour towards each other; occasionally it was a function of specific disturbance in one boy. The same was true when one boy borrowed money from another with no intention of returning it. However thefts from the staff were quite rare and had a different quality and intensity from the boys' thefts from each other. Only two boys out of the twenty-one were ever involved in episodes such as these. One boy (after he had left the house to live in lodgings), stole a sum of money by sneaking into the warden's flat. Although we saw this as a type of stealing which followed the boy's feelings that the warden had rejected him, we nevertheless reported it to the police. Otherwise it would be as if we colluded in the action and compliantly agreed that the boy was justified in it. He was put on probation. Another boy who loudly and constantly denied his need for the unit, repeatedly took small articles from the assistant warden. We saw this as a pathetic attempt at identification as well as hostility; he was a boy who constantly made jokes of a homosexual nature about himself and was always saying, 'You do love me, don't you.' These thefts were dealt with in the context of the house meetings and in one-to-one relationships before the boy was able to contain this type of aggression.

In relation to the adults in their immediate world the boys in the house meetings initially expressed feelings of primitive envy and greed. They fantasied the enormous affluence of the psychiatrist, which allowed them to be as demanding as they wished with no feelings of guilt. They had similar feelings towards the resident staff. In the house meetings it was possible for the boys to understand these attitudes and ultimately, if intermittently, they became more considerate.

The boys were not initially at all destructive of the furniture of the house. In the first eighteen months the only damage of significance was an accidental fire. A boy fell asleep on the couch with a lighted cigarette in his hand; fortunately little damage was done. After the first two years of the project, the furnishings began to wear out and the decoration of the house became shabby. The boys redecorated their own bedrooms, which remained well looked after, and also one of the downstairs rooms. The other rooms then began to deteriorate faster than was explicable on the basis of normal wear and tear. The matter was thrashed out in the house meetings, but it was only when we redecorated, and refurbished the furniture, that the episodes of minor destructiveness ceased.

It is self-evident that the boys we are describing would need again and again to test out the social structure. Each of these tests provided further growing-points for the system as a whole. The boys would intermittently come out in a rash of disturbed behaviour in relationship to each other, but gradually the way of life we wished to create became implicit in the house.

We did not expect the boys to behave in a manner that was socially aberrant either for their age or for their social group. Thus we almost always had difficulty in getting them to look after the garden and they cordially disliked helping with household chores, which was asked of them only at the weekend.

THE SOCIALIZATION OF THE BOYS

The initial aetiological classification of delinquency carried the implication that the psychological adjustment of human beings should be considered from three interrelated aspects. The way one relates to oneself, to the immediate family, and to the community at large. Any assessment of improvement has to consider all these determinants, and to pick out a change in one and to claim this as an overall improvement may be highly fallacious. One determinant of antisocial behaviour which must be present, whatever other aetiological roots exist, is the attempt on the part of an individual to resolve an internal conflict and to avoid the experience of anxiety. In 'personality delinquents' we might then theoretically expect that stopping one type of disturbed behaviour without a resolution of the psychological difficulties will lead to the appearance of another. However, this need not necessarily be the case. An individual's experience of anxiety and state of internal psychological equilibrium also depend on the human environment in which he lives. His perception of stress or emotional support arising from the outside world will affect what happens when symptoms disappear. If the human relationships which are experienced help to resolve his internal conflict and give his weak ego support, either by what they are felt to be doing, or by specific psychotherapeutic intervention, one set of symptoms may disappear without the appearance of others. It is conceivable, and this is particularly the case during the adolescent phase of human development, when the personality is both plastic and hypersensitive to the outside world, that the disappearance of a set of symptoms may lead to such a positively perceived response that there is an automatic resolution of internal difficulties. This is more likely to occur when the individual is able to invest his emotional energies in people or objects outside himself, less likely if he cannot do so. Thus a disturbed person who is relatively affectless, hypersuspicious, and emotionally withdrawn will less probably show this positive therapeutic response.

Since many of the young men who came to Northways suffered in this way we had to expect that the decrease of their use of one set of behavioural symptoms, antisocial activity in the community at large, might lead to apparent increase in others. If they were helped to lessen their sociologically inappropriate expression of aggression, and if the deeper emotional difficulties which led to it could not be resolved, they would be likely to

173

turn their aggression either against each other or against themselves. As far as outward-turned aggression is concerned, their propensity to mutual theft has been mentioned; as this abated and as to some extent their capacity to care for others was enhanced, they were more likely to do direct aggression inwards. There was much evidence of this. In the group of twenty-one boys, three made suicidal attempts during the first fourteen months of the project. These were widely scattered in time and were not therefore a result of group contagion or the fact that in an insidious way this type of self-destructive behaviour had become part of the way of life of the social system. The attempts all occurred while the environment was still relatively unstable and not as emotionally supportive to the group as it ultimately became. They all occurred in relation to the feelings of rejection experienced by the boys when they felt deserted by their girl-friends. In view of their history of maternal deprivation, it was perhaps hardly surprising that this was a situation which they unconsciously provoked and then experienced as severely traumatic.

On the other hand, as the whole social system matured, this type of acute self-destructive attempt disappeared, and after the above episodes there were no more suicidal attempts. This does not appear to be a function of the personality types of the boys concerned, since they did not, in fact, greatly differ in this respect from a later group. The answer may be in the following:

A suicidal attempt presupposes that the individual has very low self-esteem. Human beings tend to see themselves as worthwhile if they have good identification figures; for boys this means having fathers or father-surrogates who have a status in society at large. For example, it is probable that one reason for the fact that delinquency is commoner in low-status groups is that individuals from this stratum of society do not have a positive relationship with law-abiding, supporting parent figures whom they consider valuable. As the project continued, it developed a stability and value in society that was obvious to the boys. As we began to work more effectively with their aggressive feelings, they began to develop a positive relationship with the whole new social system, the staff, and the psychiatrist. The fact that these people, whom the boys perceived as being of high status, were felt to be caring for them, raised the boys' self-esteem. In addition, this positive relationship created controls by identification. As the boys gave up their aggressive acts against society, they began to develop a feeling of self-respect, and so their basic feelings of inferiority were lessened. It became more likely that the internal conflict between 'I am worthless' and 'I am valuable' was almost automatically resolved.

This increasing security was evident in many ways; as the project continued boys were able to be far more open about their difficulties. However, one way in which the boys continued to be vulnerable was in their tendency to produce psychosomatic complaints. For their age-group they had a remarkable history of minor accidents and minor physical illness during their stay in the house. For example:

When first seen, a nineteen-year-old boy, admitted after the project had been in existence for two years, was described in the initial interview by the psychiatrist as follows:

'He is a short plump boy with a rather pallid blotchy complexion. He limped into my office and handed me a letter which I opened, and only then realized that it was not addressed to me. He was bandaged on his left hand. He told me that he had had a series of tattoos removed by plastic surgery. These tattoos were apparently of naked women and seemingly he had been persuaded to have plastic surgery in borstal because of their obscene nature.

'He has the superficial charm that one sometimes sees in borstal boys. He was very polite, very positive, and expressed very strong wishes to go to Northways. I told him something of the way of life there and told him of the few rules we had devised. We then had a discussion as to whether or not he trusted me. He said he did, but immediately asked me whether there were any regulations about what sort of clothes he might wear.

I interpreted to him that in fact he really was not trusting me. 'He told me that he had a stormy career in borstal. For the first months there he had been bad-tempered and rebellious, and again he was like this when he did not get his 'grade' tie. He said that he now had his temper under control. He obviously has an immense stake in being discharged from borstal very soon. I suggested to him that perhaps if his scars were not yet properly healed he would not be able to come out immediately. I don't think he really heard me. He has no job-training and has the vague idea of perhaps becoming a male nurse because somebody suggested it to him. He is aware that he is inadequately trained for this. At one time he was, he says, an electrical engineer, and he wondered vaguely whether he might be "put into that" (his words) or ultimately "into boilers".

'The general summing-up is that he is a rather passive, dependent young man who, from time to time, will have outbursts of aggression. He is still quite attached to his "mum" but he feels that if he goes back home he will certainly fight with his brother and father.'

On psychological testing he was thought to be just intelligent enough to be admitted to the unit, his I.Q. being 90; he was also a poor reader. His social judgement was extremely weak and he had no conception of the responsibilities of social living. He was thought to be capable of semi-skilled work, providing it was done under supervision. The psychologist was struck by his difficulties in handling his aggressive feelings and the tenuousness of his emotional control. He seemed unable to integrate experience from the outside world and it was suggested that he was in fact suffering from a borderline schizophrenic process.

During his stay in Northways of fifteen weeks' duration he constantly complained of his scars, which were well healed, of suffering from eczema, and he had imaginary sore throats. He kept inventing stories of how he needed to be hospitalized. When the local practitioner would not accept his tale of physical illness he felt an angry despair.

Another way in which the group externalized their aggressive feelings was in their relationship to girls. Over half the group who had lived in the unit were known by us to be actively promiscuous, and their general attitude to girls has already been mentioned. They were unaware of the hostility in their promiscuity, but it was clear that their attitude was that girls were there to be used. We have also mentioned their hyper-suspiciousness of the motives of female staff, and the ease with which they were seen as prying and destructive people. As these boys resolved their difficulties with women, to some extent through working with the warden, they became less promiscuous and many of them married.

A self-destructive technique which was widely used by the group was the way they handled their own economic life. They found it difficult not to waste such money as they earned. By this it is not meant that from an outsider's viewpoint their money was squandered, but rather that the objects they bought only gave them transient satisfaction. They were quite unable to save for a holiday or a car, for both of which they yearned, and some boys earned enough to have made these wishes realistic. Apart from this difficulty many of them seemed unable to keep a job. They were bad timekeepers, became easily bored, and often would stay off work because of minor psychosomatic complaints.

Just as they found it difficult to become emotionally involved with people and things, so they had the same problems with anything they themselves might produce – their work. An important concept about human development is that in order to be productive, men have to come to terms with their feelings of envy for women's productivity. By this we mean that the small boy has to come to terms with the fact that, unlike his sister, he cannot have babies as his mother does, and there is evidence for this from watching the play of small children. These boys had had shocking experiences in their relationships with their mothers and thus had not been able to come to terms with their own masculinity. The only masculine productivity some of them had was the ability to conceive children, which was looked upon as an important status symbol.

Thus their inability to work constructively had at least three determinants. They had never been trained to do this, they had not come to terms with themselves as productive young men, and, finally, they used their work inability as a self-destructive technique. Instead of externalizing their aggressive feelings they attacked themselves. One boy said to the warden one day:

'I get so angry with you that I think up schemes by which I might hurt you. I stayed off work so you would be worried, but I always end up by hurting myself. I wish I could find a way of hurting you without hurting me.'

THE BOYS' RELATIONSHIP TO FOOD AND MILK

The point has been made that the group in Northways were suffering from a variety of psychological syndromes all of which had as an aetiological root emotional deprivation. Because of this we deliberately did not try to set a rigid budget for food when the project started. Our attitude was that we did not know what the group would eat and when. We believed that because of their long years in institutions, in some of which food withdrawal such as a bread-and-water diet is still used as a punishment, this was an area in which we should be permissive. We did not intend to serve highly expensive food, but the boys could have as much as they liked and they could eat between meals. To use technical terminology, since these boys had been orally deprived we believed it was likely that they would seek oral satisfaction. If it was not provided by us, we thought that the boys would either drink or smoke excessively; alternatively, it was not impossible that they might become addicted to drugs. Since we were prepared to allow the boys to bring guests in to meals and have ex-Northways boys return similarly, we knew that the food costs per head would be high. Food consumption based on twelve residents and staff throughout the period of the project, excluding milk, cost approximately 50s. per head per week; this compares with the allowance for all foods of 24s. 3d. per head in an approved school.

Therapeutic Techniques: The social system and socialization

Food costs did not appear to vary very much with the number of boys in residence. They fluctuated somewhat with a complex of factors such as unemployment, tensions in the house, pilfering by visitors, the number of visitors, boys leaving and arriving, and the number of boys in for lunch. It is impossible in retrospect to draw out one factor, say unemployment, and claim that it had a very important influence. If the figures are looked at closely, high and low consumption occurred independently of high and low employment.

When foods the boys liked were in short supply they were unable to spin them out; instead they would tend to grab what they could before another boy got there. They did this to the extent of hiding food they did not want immediately, which would go bad unless someone discovered the hiding-place. These were immediate problems when a boy was first discharged from borstal; they tended to taper off as he became more secure with prolonged residence.

A surprising finding was the large milk consumption. Milk consumption per head per boy in residence varied overall between two and three pints per day. At one period the boys were consuming four pints of milk daily each. Had the project taken place in the United States, this might not have been so remarkable; in Britain, when the adolescent is not normally a large milk-drinker, the figures are more significant. A close look at milk consumption shows the influence of various factors. If the disturbance of the boys was clearly confined to the house meeting, milk consumption fell; there was then less oral 'acting out'. For example, after one house meeting in which the psychiatrist felt that he had spent an evening dealing with grossly psychotic material, over the following week each boy consumed a pint of milk a day less. Whenever the warden went on holiday milk consumption rose dramatically in the two weeks before her departure; it fell immediately after she had gone and the boys' tension had subsided. When a boy was arrested for larceny, milk consumption for the other boys rose to an all-time high; when his recall was finally ordered three weeks later it again fell. On two occasions when there was a shortage of milk owing to bad weather, the following weeks the milk consumption rose by a pint a day per boy; the same occurred when on one occasion milk ran out.

In the last six months of the project the average age of the boys in the house fell from twenty to just over eighteen years. With the older age group rises in overall food costs could be accounted for by a rise in milk consumption; for the younger group food costs tended to fall as milk costs rose. In an overall way more milk was consumed when the average age of the boys in the house was younger. Under stress, in our situation, a young man of twenty would add milk to his diet, he would not eat less; boys of eighteen more easily behaved in a regressive infantile manner and drank milk instead of eating.

With the younger group in residence there was a period of three months in which job turnover was at a minimum, the boys were not stealing from each other, and so far as we know there was a minimum of sexual promiscuity. Initially during this period the group was more verbally aggressive with the staff and more openly critical and angry with the psychiatrist. The milk consumption then was at its highest ever, rising to twenty-nine pints per boy per week. As the boys became less anxious and less aggressive, the milk consumption steadily fell, and it became necessary drastically to reduce the amount we bought. With this same group, as a holiday period drew near for the staff, consumption rose again.

It was possible to pinpoint tension by the milk consumption taken on a daily basis. On one occasion two boys appeared in court; the day this occurred consumption in the house rose from twenty pints to twenty-seven. On one day the boys were all tense and excited, feeling that their jobs were no good; that day consumption was twenty-seven pints, two days later when they felt at ease it fell to fourteen pints. The day before a boy was told to leave for having a girl sleep in the house, milk consumption was nineteen pints, the day he left it rose to twenty-four, the following day it was again nineteen.

Several conclusions can be drawn from these figures for milk and food. Alcoholism was never a problem in the house; there was less drunkenness among the Northways boys, we suspect, than in an equivalent group of university students of the same age. We have mentioned that some boys for a short time after leaving borstal became temporarily quite fat, but in an overall way they put on weight, muscle, and breadth in an appropriate manner after this initial flurry.

So far in this chapter we have considered various ways in which the Northways group acted out their internal conflicts; it is now appropriate to consider the evidence for psychological maturation. One key issue is the way the boys responded to the anxiety associated with separation when they left the unit.

Apart from the boy who was reconvicted while living in the house, three of the group left without any prior discussion of the possibility of their doing so, either in the house meetings or with the staff. Two of these departed of their own accord, abruptly and with no notice; one was asked to leave after striking another boy. These three boys were all reconvicted: two of them five months after leaving; one after one month. Of the remaining thirteen boys who left, five of them went for a short period of time, found they could not manage, and returned to the house. Of this group, at the time of writing, ten have made a successful adjustment without any reconvictions; two were reconvicted, one of whom was institutionalized, the other put on probation. With all these boys there was discussion with them well in advance of their leaving. Three left to marry, the rest were told by the psychiatrist, some two to four months before they actually went, that we thought that they were ready to leave. During this period they talked of and demonstrated their anxiety, but, whatever they did in the house, once we had come to the conclusion that a boy was ready to leave we stuck to the decision. As has been mentioned, had we not done so, there would have been so much secondary gain from any antisocial behaviour in which they might have become involved, that we would have created in the community the attitude that all that was needed to stay was to 'mess up' in some way.

Of the thirteen Northways boys who have made a successful adjustment, nine have married; this compares with three marriages out of eleven such boys in the homeless control group, five out of fourteen in the home control. It is apparent, since only one of the homeless boys who married have been reconvicted, that the ability to marry carries with it a greater chance of making a successful community adjustment. Four of the boys who married did so because the girls were pregnant, but there was no situation in the house in which this happened and the boys did not wish to marry. At the time of writing, two of these families have a child. When the boys married we were concerned about what seemed to be their immaturity, nevertheless six of these new families have set up homes of their own, three in unfurnished flats. This is no mean feat at a time of acute housing shortage in a large metropolitan centre in which rents tend to be exorbitant. From visiting the boys' homes it is clear that in many ways they have made a positive identification with the rooms that they saw and lived with in Northways. Their homes are clean, neat, and tidy; the boys are constructive around the house, for instance, one boy built his own kitchen. They all have a television set which has been rented; the Northways set was similarly acquired. The boys are well fed by their wives, and there have been no cases of infidelity or excessive drunkenness among these new husbands. There is evidence that the boys have identified with the caring-for attitude that we attempted to create in the unit. Only one of the boys married in a church, the first boy to marry. When he married the rest of the group at the time complained that there was too much to drink at the wedding reception. Of the ten couples who married, three required help from Northways over the first few weeks with food, but this has never been more than a transient need. Four of the couples visited Northways from time to time together, both fathers bring their babies, and the husbands come in alone whenever they have a tiff with their wives. The relationship of these boys to their infants would indicate something of the strength of their identification with women. It did not appear that they were consciously being competitive with their wives, but rather that they were automatically casting themselves in a maternal role. The usual father in our society appears to enjoy his children when they obviously respond to him as a person. These boys appeared to reject their babies at this point, at any rate relative to the intensity of the initial 'mothering' they gave them. The wives, in their turn, used the warden to discuss any difficulties they experienced with their husbands and problems of baby care were also relevantly discussed.

All the boys who are currently living in the community and who have had no reconvictions show clinical signs of increasing maturity. They have more self-respect, they are not on the delinquent fringe of the community, they do not show evidence of being anti-authority, and there is a steady improvement through the months in their work records.

CHAPTER XI

Causes of Failure in Northways

THE EVENTS that led to boys committing crimes while living in
Northways throw light on the treatment requirements of
delinquent adolescents, which might, if satisfied, make for better
results than are currently obtained in the penal system. Although
awareness of this is not widespread at the present time, if enough
is known of the home background and psychological state of a
given human being, and of the environment in which he lives, it
is sometimes possible to predict the type of situation in which he
is likely to commit a crime. Sexual murderers, for example, can
be diagnosed before the event in many cases, but this does not
necessarily mean that treatment facilities will be available.

The more that is known of the personality disturbances that
are likely to produce antisocial behaviour, the better is the chance
of successful therapy, and a specific study of the boys who were
reconvicted either while living in Northways or after they left
throws some light on the aetiology of delinquent behaviour.
Even with the small number of boys who committed crimes,
eight in all, it was possible to differentiate different types of
personality with different treatment needs. Since the Northways
system could not treat these boys appropriately, failure with them
was probably inevitable.

Four of the boys in the unit who were reconvicted were
remarkably similar personality types. The first of these boys had
the following story:

This was a boy who was admitted to Northways at the age of
twenty. He had marked facial acne, was tall and round-

shouldered, and looked unprepossessing. He had a history of nine previous convictions before going to borstal. His criminal record started when he was ten, one year after the death of his father. All his institutional experience was in approved schools (three years eight months) or borstal (two years). He had a history of asthma and a family (mother and step-father) who were themselves antisocial. He attended a child guidance clinic for one year at the age of eight. During his stay in borstal he had a miniature gallows on his locker on which he would hang a succession of 'screws'.

On initial interview for the unit his hyper-suspiciousness, feelings of isolation, and general coldness were most strikingly evident. He was emotionally flat and whatever idea he was expressing he showed no feeling: he was affectless.

When he arrived in Northways he was often silent in house meetings or appeared very late. When he did talk it was only to insist that everything should be locked up because no one was to be trusted. When this was unacceptable to the rest of the boys, he became bitter and angry and announced that he would not stay. He told many stories of how he and his family success-fully swindled bookmakers prior to his borstal committal. He believed that everyone in the house was against him and stayed out as much as possible. He was aware of his own antisocial impulses and shortly after saying to the psychiatrist, 'I don't want anyone to care for me because if they do I will let them down', he left against our advice. He went to live with his mother, who had initially said that she wanted nothing to do with him.

The psychiatrist noted at the time of his departure:

'I predict that he will not be able to make a successful adjust-ment; the only helpful approach I would envisage is that he might be able to come back to Northways if trouble be sensed by his supervising officer before it occurs.'

The boy had stayed in the unit for seven weeks. Twelve weeks later he was fined for a motoring offence, and in the following year he had two more similar convictions for which he was fined. Nineteen months later he was imprisoned for larceny for six months and immediately after discharge from prison he was again fined for using insulting words and behaviour.

The second of the four boys had a story as follows:

This was a rather handsome well-built youth who was admitted to Northways at the age of nineteen. He had a history of numerous convictions prior to borstal, including arson at the ages of eight and twelve. He had also been involved in housebreaking. He had a conviction for violence, which he did not mention in his initial interview. The boy had been deserted by his mother at the age of one year and had lived in children's homes since. As soon as he left his last children's home at the age of sixteen he began to get into trouble and continued thus until he was placed in borstal. During his stay there he was in trouble twice, once for bad language and once for wrestling on a bed (his story).

In his clinical interviews he had a striking inability to be spontaneous and he covered his extreme hypersuspiciousness by emotional withdrawal. He was extremely guarded and was unable to express an opinion. He was flat emotionally, quite affectless, and gave the impression of retreating into a private world of fantasy. It appeared on psychological examination that he would respond with aggressive violence if he saw his tenuous concept of his own masculinity being threatened.

In Northways he continued to be apparently passive and secretive and he was involved in receiving stolen property. This fact emerged just as he left to go into the army.

This boy had stayed twenty-two weeks, maintaining the same job throughout. Just as with the first boy, he never appeared in this time to establish a relationship with any of the staff, including the psychiatrist. It was clear from an interview with the latter when he was on leave two months after induction, that he had continued while in the service to receive stolen cigarettes. This apparently gave him a feeling of being powerful and putting one

Causes of Failure in Northways

over on society. His behaviour was known to the other boys in Northways and it appeared that they gained vicarious satisfaction from his actions. Fifteen months later he was sentenced for larceny and assault while on leave. Apparently a policeman had approached him while he was with his girl-friend, and he had struck the man in the course of his arrest.

The third similar boy in Northways had an equivalent background but was, in fact, able to make a highly tenuous relationship. His attitude to crime was the same but he did not in fact move away from the unit for many months. On the one hand, he expressed the feeling that it was his only hope; on the other, it was 'an easy kip'. He had two reconvictions during his stay. He was fined for travelling on the underground without paying his fare, and he was bound over for carrying an offensive weapon. He covered his lonely affectionless feelings with a façade of indifference. Although capable of superficial talk, he found it difficult to relate to people, and it was as if one were talking to him through a glass. Although of average intelligence, he was assessed in borstal as being less than average, and he received no vocational training.

He spent much of his time out of the house on mysterious errands in which he was mostly gambling. He was more able to contact people than the other two boys but his prognosis for a non-institutional adjustment is equally doubtful.

Criminal behaviour was part of a way of life for these boys; from it they obtained immediate gratification with no consideration of the consequences. They covered a great deal of internal confusion with a withdrawn, affectless approach to the external world. They ran away in reality and emotionally from interpersonal relationships. With neither of these boys did one feel that delinquent behaviour in general was related to an attempted resolution of an immediate emotional conflict; they were in fact people who sought gratification from possessions rather than relationships and had no conscious guilt about it.

It was possible with these boys, and with the fourth, to prognosticate further trouble because they were projecting 'We are not

187

to be trusted' to 'They are not to be trusted'. Their paranoid anxiety was so great that they could not make a human relationship in an open system which they could leave at any time. In addition to this, the first boy had the worst prognosis because delinquency was acceptable in his family and social background; in the aetiological hierarchy described in Chapter I he was a personality, intrafamilial, and situational delinquent.

Another three boys in the unit who became overtly delinquent stole only in relation to specific, and obvious, conflicts. The first of these boys had the following story:

> He was a curly-haired, neatly dressed, pleasant young man of nineteen who missed his first appointment to discuss coming to the unit by being seventy-five minutes late. He refused psychological testing because of his fear of what it would show. He had been in institutions for fifteen years and did not know his parents. He had many convictions for larceny and had been in an approved school prior to borstal. He had an air of superficial braggadocio but when anxious would become pale, tense, and frightened. Shortly after his arrival in Northways he had an hysterical episode when a girl-friend, whom he constantly provoked to do so, rejected him. He took an overdose of aspirins. The boy would provocatively stir up other people so that they became extremely rejecting. When this happened he became depressed, quit his job, and stole anything he could lay his hands on. When he was caught he would be extremely tormented and the episode would then subside. Furthermore he was an inveterate gambler and always lost. If he saw a boy as being more unsure than himself he would attempt to order him around. He lived in the house for nineteen months. After one year he left for eight weeks because of a failure to pay his rent, but returned when it became clear that he could not manage.
>
> His episodes of theft in Northways became further and further apart in time, and ultimately we put it to him that he seemed ready to leave. He accepted this and, although we made many

interpretations to him about the anger he must feel, he denied doing so. He said that he was glad to go because the boys in the house were now too young for him. Just before he left he 'borrowed' the psychiatrist's raincoat which he kept forgetting to return. Six months after his departure, while visiting the house, he sneaked into the warden's flat and stole about £15. The theft was reported to the police; he was caught and put on probation for three years. It was made clear to the magistrate by the supervising officer that we thought that the aetiology of the episode was associated with his disturbed reaction to feeling rejected.

The second of these three boys was separated from his mother when he was two and was looked after by a foster-mother until he was nine. He was then moved to a new home because he was too old for the first. He did not settle in two new foster-homes and was then again moved to a children's home. While there he ran away and in order to do so took a bicycle. For this 'offence' and because he was now a difficult management problem he was committed to an approved school. After leaving school, his second offence was 'taking and driving away a motor vehicle'; he released the brake of a car standing on a hill and moved it several yards. He entered the Air Force and while on leave stole in rapid succession, sweets, a torch, a coat, a pedal cycle, and money from a gas-meter; he was committed for borstal training.

One comment on his borstal records reads:

'A lonely rather pathetic individual who had suffered from a great deal of emotional deprivation.'

Another writer put:

'A small pathetic-looking lad who has thrown away what for him would be the best chance in life I feel – the R.A.F. He will finish this sentence without any idea as to where he is going to live and the future looks very bleak indeed.'

This was not a situation in which his syndrome of theft was unrecognized; a borstal housemaster wrote:

'He has done a good deal of petty stealing in his day and the element of affection substitution can be inferred. He escapes from self-criticism by seeking distraction in some foolish escapade.'

This boy had come to Northways when he was just eighteen and his first action was to buy a bicycle. He could not tolerate the emotional deprivation associated with separation, and was unable to weather the summer holidays of the warden and the psychiatrist. He responded with an outburst of community theft and was recalled to borstal. He was quickly released, but the following Easter the same reaction occurred again and he received a new borstal sentence.

The last of these three boys was a boy of nineteen who had been in children's homes of various types from the age of five. He had entered the army at the age of fifteen and was sent to borstal at the age of seventeen for his first offence, breaking and entering, while on leave. He was potentially of much higher intelligence than his borstal rating and the psychologist in his pre-Northways assessment said of him:

'A typically institutionalized young man who defends himself from the painful repetition of early deprivation by withdrawal from others, apathy, and inhibition. Potentially of good average intelligence, his effectiveness is impaired when he is required to work in a situation in which he is actively involved with someone else.'

The comment was made about him that only over a piece of work could he make a human relationship. He would need a protected environment to prevent him from walking out of situations in which he would feel threatened by this: at the same time he yearned for it. At the same series of interviews the psychiatrist wrote independently:

'This is a rather pleasant, well-built young man who struck me as being desolately empty. It seems rather distressing that no effort, so far as I can gather, has been made to train him in any trade. In the unit it will be rather like trying to fill up an empty vessel which is full of holes. He will respond extremely badly to deprivation if he does manage to make any tentative relationships.'

The last two boys on both occasions stole together. They showed common personality difficulties and at the time of these thefts they had a common emotional problem at a conscious and an unconscious level. They were thus acting out their difficulties together in a small delinquent gang formation. The latter boy, being reconvicted and returned to borstal, wrote to the warden:

'Dear Mrs. D., I am writing this letter to let you know how sorry I am for letting you all down, and deceiving you, but if this is any consolation to you and you accept my apologies, I will be more than greatly pleased. As you know I am in borstal now and if any one gives me a second chance in life I won't deserve it. I only pray to God that the next time I get out I will lead a more diligent course of life. Well I must close now. Be sure and tell the boys that I am asking for them.
Yours sincerely, ...'.

Whenever they felt rejected by significant people in their lives the reaction of these three boys was to steal. This was always associated with other signs of disturbed behaviour, confusion, depression, or anger.

Certain therapeutic conclusions can be drawn about these seven boys. The first four ran away from making interpersonal relationships, the second three reacted to 'separation anxiety' with destructive behaviour. The possibility of physical containment was thus necessary. The boys who were unable to make relationships need a social system that would be able to offer them the equivalent therapeutic milieu to Northways, but which could have contained them over the initial period of potentially severe anxiety which would have occurred if they made a relationship. Emotional withdrawal would then have replaced physical withdrawal, but this can possibly be dealt with psychotherapeutically.

For the second group of three the hypothesis is that their only hope is to have the psychotherapeutic relationships that obtained in Northways, with the possibility of giving them physical security at times of stress, to contain their aggressive and self-destructive acting-out. Unfortunately at the present time neither the borstal system nor Northways can provide this combination. The recognition of this problem is not peculiar to the unit, but adequate therapeutic facilities for such boys as these are effectively unobtainable. The borstal comment about one boy was accurate:

> 'If he could form a trusting relationship with an adult he could respect, we might see an agreeable development. He shies from real attachments.'

The skill to make this possible does not usually exist in a treatment setting with the possibility of open and closed supervision, at the same time enabling a boy to keep the same relationships with people and understand his difficulties with them. These are not untreatable boys although, because of the social reality, their current prognosis for a successful life adjustment is not good.

A notable feature of the reconvicted boys in the homeless control group is that once they break down they do not keep out of further trouble for very long. The boy in the second group who stole the money from the warden committed no further offences after the episode described, and seven months later was still in a steady job. Thus, although from a statistical viewpoint he is a 'failure', from a psychosocial standpoint he is currently a success. Given his state of disturbance, in association with his leaving the unit, it was probably inevitable that, partly as a protest against being rejected, partly as a wish to demonstrate his incompetence and need to return, he would commit an antisocial act. If we had responded to the plea implicit in the theft and taken him back or if the magistrate's court had reinstitutionalized him, then again all his regressive dependency would have been revived. The eighth and last boy convicted during the first two and a half years of the project was eighteen. He is one of the group of personality delinquents who is psychotic, and he was, without doubt, suffering from a chronic schizophrenic reaction. In the highly structured environment of borstal he presented an effective if brittle façade, and his clinical illness, which was overtly obvious when he lived in the community at large, was not so evident there. Because he was so inadequate in his social adjustment, he was recalled to borstal from Northways after an episode of larceny for which he was given a conditional discharge. He could not get a job and could not keep money given to him by the National Assistance Board long enough to pay his room rent.

The following letter was written by the psychiatrist to the prison medical officer when he was returned to borstal.

'When he was first seen here in clinical examination he had a pseudo-frankness, and my first impression of him was that he had a capacity to relate to other people. However, the suspicious thing clinically about this first interview was that he talked extremely openly of his sexual difficulties and he was quite frank about the fact that he hated both men and women. On psychological testing he had an I.Q. of approximately 105 (verbal I.Q. 104, performance 102 on the Wechsler scale). The psychologist was of the opinion that he was suffering from a chronic schizophrenic reaction. She felt this particularly because he was unable to make human relationships, he showed a detachment of feeling and he grossly perseverated on the test responses on the Rorschach. By this I mean that if he gave a response to one card on the test he carried the same response over to others, with no impact created by the difference between them.

During the four months he has been in Northways he has shown no capacity to learn by experience, he is impulse-ridden, and his judgement is extremely poor. He clearly has no concept of the difference between right and wrong, particularly when he is under stress. Any action is justified if it meets his immediate needs and he is not aware of the realistic implications of what does . . . It is possible of course that the details of his maladjustment will be lost in the institutional setting . . . quite frankly, even under the M'Naughten rules, this boy should be considered insane.'

In this letter it was suggested that he should be committed to a hospital under the Mental Health Act. He was kept for a few weeks in the prison hospital, and then sent on for routine borstal training. After discharge he did well for five months and was then reconvicted.

One of the problems of the 'open door' policy of mental hospitals is that if community resources are inadequate certain severely ill people move from one type of institution, the hospital, to another, the prison. These are often personalities who can make an institutional adjustment with the support they obtain from that type of environment. This boy falls into that category and one would predict a chronic institutional adjustment for him, or, he will use many community resources to subsist marginally in society.

CHAPTER XII

Comparative Results of the Northways and Control Groups

A CRITERION of the success of the project was whether or not the Northways boys had a better chance of not being reconvicted than they would have had if they had undergone routine after-care. However, since recall to borstal is a discretionary move, within legal limits, of the Borstal Divisional authorities, the number of boys recalled is of significance in assessing the validity of the results. If, for example, a number of Northways boys were returned to borstal without a history of having been reconvicted, the results become suspect. It might be said that their recall prevented further reconvictions. Since it is the proper duty of all personnel concerned in rehabilitation to protect society, and it is a false dichotomy from a therapeutic viewpoint to separate this from the care of the individual, such recalls might have been necessary.

Three boys were recalled to borstal during the two and a half years of the project, but only one was in fact recalled without a new conviction. One reason for the recall of this boy (who was mentioned in Chapter I), was to protect him, because the psychiatric facilities of the community were inadequate. When it was necessary to recall him it was hoped that such facilities as exist in the borstal system might be helpful. His recall lasted about three months and he has continued since his discharge to make a highly successful adjustment in the community at large.

The two other boys who were recalled had been reconvicted. A boy mentioned in Chapter XI, who received a conditional discharge from the courts for larceny, was so severely disturbed psychologically that he was returned to borstal. One other boy was recalled for a short period of time after a bout of larceny offences, a necessary step, otherwise we should have appeared to him to be colluding in his antisocial behaviour. He returned to Northways within three months.

A reconviction is not necessarily indicative of the value of the work done with the boys, because failure to return to a court of law does not demonstrate that a boy will be a reasonably mature member of society. It does not even mean that further crimes have not been committed. Conversely, committing a further offence does not necessarily indicate a failure of significant psychosocial maturation. Nevertheless, the only possible comparison that can be made between the control and the Northways groups involves the number of boys reconvicted. Any specific investigation of the psychological adjustment of individuals in the control groups would certainly contaminate the results, because the procedure with them would have ceased to be routine.

It will be recalled that we planned to compare the Northways group with an equivalent group of homeless boys who went through the normal after-care procedure, and with a group of boys equivalent in all other respects except that they had homes. All the Northways group were supervised by the supervising officers of Borstal After-Care; of the homeless control group, twenty-one were supervised by such officers, eight by probation officers; of the group with homes, all were supervised by probation officers. Two and a half years after the start of the project, a total of seventy-nine boys had been discharged from borstal in the three groups. The average period of time spent living in the community from discharge was 19·4 months per boy. The overall reconviction figures were as follows:

Home Control: thirteen out of twenty-nine boys at risk
reconvicted 45%

Homeless Control: nineteen out of twenty-nine boys at
  risk reconvicted 65%
Northways: eight out of twenty-one boys at risk reconvicted 38%

Although not a sufficiently large number of boys had been
free for a two-year period, certain trends emerge from these
figures. The Northways group is doing better than the other
homeless boys. If, at the time of the general survey, the eleven
boys who had been out of Northways for more than two years are
considered, the overall reconviction figure for this group is three
out of eleven.

TABLE 4 PERCENTAGE RECONVICTION RATES OF BOYS AT
RISK FOR VARIOUS PERIODS

Group	6 months	12 months	18 months	24 months
Home Control	45%	46%	63%	67%
	(13 of 29)	(12 of 26)	(12 of 19)	(10 of 15)
Homeless Control	65%	65%	67%	61%
	(19 of 29)	(17 of 26)	(14 of 21)	(8 of 13)
Northways	38%	33%	36%	28%
	(8 of 21)	(6 of 18)	(5 of 14)	(3 of 11)

Beyond twenty-four months the figures are so far too small to have any significance.

A more statistically valid comparison of the results is possible
if the number of boys at risk over given periods of time after discharge from borstal is considered.

It will be seen from the table that the Northways boys appear to
have a better chance of not being reconvicted, twenty-four months
after discharge from borstal, than the other two groups. If the
period at which the reconvicted boys remain at liberty is considered, it is apparent that reconviction is more likely to occur in
the first nine months of freedom than in the second. In this period
89% of the reconvictions of the homeless boys took place, 54%

197

of the boys with homes, and 62% of the Northways boys. If the boys who had left the unit are considered, six out of seven of the reconvictions which then occurred took place in the first nine months.

Table 6 opposite demonstrates this.

From these results Northways would appear to provide a much-needed transitional experience from living in borstal to living in the community for boys who are homeless. The two boys who were reconvicted within five months of their release from

TABLE 5   OFFENCES COMMITTED

Offences	Northways Pre-borstal	Northways Post-borstal	Homeless Pre-borstal	Homeless Post-borstal	Home Pre-borstal	Home Post-borstal
Theft (Larceny, breaking and entering)	59 (75%)	10 (59%)	80 (77%)	23 (48%)	70 (65%)	10 (40%)
Taking and driving away a motor vehicle	8	0	7	5	22	5
Sexual	3	0	0	0	0	0
Violent	1	1	4	4	1	4
Miscellaneous	7	6	13	16	15	6
Totals	78	17	109	48	108	25
Convictions per boy	3·7	·80	3·7	1·6	3·7	·86

borstal spent the shortest period of time there, respectively seven and sixteen weeks. The reasons for this were considered in Chapter XI.

If the change in the type of crimes committed is reviewed, the following figures emerge (see *Table 5*).

It is not possible from this table to ascribe any necessary significance to the fall in the number of reconvictions per boy after discharge from borstal, but there is a significant difference between the figures for homeless boys who underwent routine after-care and the Northways group.

198

TABLE 6 ANALYSIS OF RECONVICTIONS (BY INTERVAL AT RISK AND NUMBERS AT RISK)

Months after discharge from Borstal	1	2	3	4	5	6	7	8	9	10	11	12	13	14	15	16	17	18	19	20	21	22	23	24	25	26	27	28	30	Total Recons.
Home Control No. Recon.	1		1		3			1	1	1		1						2		1									1	13
No. of those at risk	29	29	29	29	29	29	29	29	29	28	26	26	23	23	23	22	20	19	19	18	15	15	15	15	13	12	12	12	10	
Homeless Control No. Recon.	1	1	2	5	2	2	1	1	2				1									1								19
No. of those at risk	29	29	29	29	29	29	29	29	28	27	27	26	25	23	23	23	22	21	20	20	17	15	14	13	12	11	10	9	7	
Northways No. Recon.					2	1	1	1	1				1					1												8
No. of those at risk	21	21	21	21	21	21	21	21	21	20	19	18	17	17	17	15	14	14	14	13	11	11	11	11	10	8	8	8	7	

Months after discharge from Northways	1	2	3	4	5	6	7	8	9	10	11	12	13	14	15	16	17	18	19	20	21	22	23	24	25	26	27	28	30	Total Recons.
No. Recon.	1	1	1									1	1												2					7
No. of those at risk	18	18	17	16	16	15	14	14	12	12	12	12	12	11	9	7	7	6	6	6	5	4	3	3	2	1	1	1	1	

These figures are from too small samples to indicate anything but possible trends, but nevertheless for a larger group they bear investigation. If the Northways boys are considered, the number of convictions for all forms of theft of property changed from 75% to 59% of the total. There is an equivalent fall in all groups, 77% to 48% for the homeless control, 65% to 40% for the home control. Taking and driving away a motor vehicle did not shift significantly as a proportion of the convictions for the other two groups and in fact is remarkably steady; no Northways boy had this as a cause of reconviction. Sexual offences, which were necessarily few because of our sampling method, disappeared with the Northways group and did not appear with the others. There is an apparent shift with crimes of violence but the same boy was involved in this from the unit as prior to borstal. Three boys from the homeless group were involved both times (the same three) and two boys from the home control. If these figures are true for larger and more significant numbers of ex-borstal boys, there is perhaps an indication that the system fails to deal satisfactorily with this type of boy of average intelligence who is so psychologically disturbed as to be aggressively violent. In earlier chapters the comment was made that boys identify with the aspects of a social system which are covert and undesirable, if they do not establish significant relationships with the staff which are understood, and if separation as a process is not worked through in an emotionally meaningful way. The study of the Northways group indicated that, as people, they emerged from borstal and other institutions with a disregard for the feelings of others, hyper-suspicious, and all too easily stimulated to aggressive fantasy. Much of the therapeutic work of the unit consisted in dealing with just these problems and our attempt to have the boys identify with an attitude that people should be cared for and cared about. We did not succeed, for reasons that have been discussed, with the violent boy, and it is perhaps then not surprising that the after-care agents failed to help the boys in the other two groups who were similarly reconvicted.

The number of 'miscellaneous offences', which includes

200

motoring offences other than 'taking and driving away', show a relative increase as a proportion of all offences after discharge from borstal. This may only be a result of the increase in age of the group. It may be valid to do a study of the relationship of the type of offence to the age of the offender on a year-by-year basis, rather than as an age group.

There are indications that the penal system as at present constituted is not helpful to some boys, if the comparative figures for boys who had been in approved schools are considered. Eleven Northways boys had previously been in such institutions; three of them were reconvicted. In the homeless control group, fourteen boys had been in approved schools; nine of them were reconvicted. In the home control group, the figure is three out of four. Once again, these figures indicate that the project was tending to reverse the trend of the institutional process which appears not to assist vulnerable individuals.

Vocational training appeared, from a consideration of individual cases in the Northways group, to have ill-prepared the boys to handle the real-life economic situation they had to face. They came to the unit, as we have said, with unrealistic expectations of their training, both as to the skill they had acquired and the amount they could expect to earn. This was a perpetual live issue with the group. Of the nine boys who received vocational training, four carried on with their trade during their stay in the house with a good deal of assistance from the staff and the supervising officer both in job placement and psychological help. These included two carpenters, one painter, and one welder. The welder, who had a history of violent crime, dropped his trade when he went into the paratroops three months after coming to Northways; he was convicted one year later for the same type of offence. Three of the boys who had received vocational training in borstal were reconvicted, the same proportion as for the group as a whole.

The hypothesis could be put forward that if the vocational training a boy had received had adequately prepared him for life outside borstal, we could expect that it would be of assistance in helping him not to be reconvicted.

201

In the homeless control group, of ten boys trained, only one, an engineering fitter, spent any time in his trade after he returned to society. Of these ten, seven were reconvicted (70%), as compared with 62% for the group as a whole. Of the boys with homes, seven received vocational training, none has been employed continuously in his trade, but three boys had some period of work in their trades. Three of this group were reconvicted (43%), as compared with 41% of the group as a whole. Since there is no statistical difference between any of these figures, and the numbers in the groups are small, it is impossible with these samples to make any assessment of the value of vocational training; to do so would involve consideration of figures for the borstal system as a whole.

Of boys in the groups who requested vocational training, nineteen out of thirty-four of the homeless boys received it, seven out of twenty-six, of those with homes. From the small number of Northways boys involved, it is apparent that a boy who asks for trade training in a specific vocation, and receives it, is more likely to carry on with it after release. For example, five of this group received the vocational training for which they asked, and four of the five carried on with their trade after release. However four of the control group of homeless youths in an equivalent position did not carry on with their trade, two boys with homes similarly involved did carry through with their jobs for a short time.

All too often the failures of the approved school service and the borstal system are blamed on to them. It is as if society implies that they have all the resources they need and it is the sheer inadequacy of the people involved which leads to disastrous results. Homeless boys are not disturbed psychologically just because they have been in institutions, their disturbance is also a function of the trauma they have experienced in their intra-familial situations. Given that we found as much psychological illness in these boys as is apparent, it is not unreasonable to suppose that a large percentage of boys with homes who commit offences, and fail to respond to borstal treatment, are themselves significantly disturbed. With the evidence from our study one wonders whether the penal system has the psychological knowledge or sophistication to cope with this. The evidence would appear to be to the contrary.

Psychiatric treatment in the borstal service would not appear, from our study, to have a significant impact on institutions. There was no evidence that the severely disturbed group we studied had been seen by a psychiatrist in the institutions to which they were sent, far less exposed to either psychological treatment or specific psychosocial manipulation of an environment designed to meet their needs. All the boys, of similar intelligence and personality profiles, had been scattered through fifteen different borstal institutions.

It would appear to be a reasonable deduction from the experience of this study that the longer a human being needs to live in institutions, or the greater the number of his previous convictions, the more likely is he to be disturbed and inadequate and the more likely is he to be again reconvicted. The boys of the Northways group who were reconvicted averaged 11·1 years in institutions as against 9·1 years for the group as a whole; 4·4 previous convictions as against 3·7.

On the other hand, it appears that the longer a boy stayed in the unit, the better was his chance of not being reconvicted. Eighteen boys left to live in the community; the seven who were reconvicted had an average duration of stay of twenty-eight weeks, the three who were reinstitutionalized in the penal system had twenty weeks as an average. For the eleven boys who were not convicted, the average duration of stay was forty-four weeks. For all nineteen boys who left, including one reconvicted from the house to borstal, the average duration of stay was thirty-nine weeks.

Another way of assessing the Northways group as against the control population is to compare their relationship to their work. We have already mentioned the inadequacy of the boys in the unit in this respect, and theoretically one would expect that the control groups might have had a lower rate of job turnover than the young men from Northways, because their reconviction rate was much higher. Unfortunately, it was not possible to get an accurate assessment of this trend but there was some evidence for it. Delinquent boys are notoriously unreliable reporters, and we could not ask the after-care personnel to keep a special check on their charges' work adjustment. If we had done so, we would have introduced another determinant, which would have meant that we were no longer comparing the treatment of the Northways group with routine after-care procedure. However, if the work record for the control groups was as poor as for the Northways boys at some stages of their stay, this would inevitably have appeared on the after-care records, and it did not.

The work record of the Northways group prior to their borstal sentences was not impressive. As has been mentioned, eight of them had more than three jobs a year and seven more than six. This would indicate that job-switching was occurring prior to their coming to the unit but, as will be seen, its frequency changed.

It should not be assumed that a young man who has a flurry of jobs immediately after leaving school is necessarily giving an indication of personality disturbance. His behaviour may follow from an appropriate wish to experiment and to find a place for himself in economic life. If, as with the Northways group, the ability to keep a job is impaired as a continuing process, it should be regarded, other relevant aspects of life also being considered, as evidence of emotional illness.

While resident in the unit, the boys had an average of ten to eleven jobs each per year. After they left, this figure fell to between six and seven; both of these are apparently considerably higher than the average of four to five jobs per year before they were committed to borstal, although the preconviction figures are based on the boys' statements, not on observed facts, and may be too low. There are indications that the longer the boys were at liberty the less frequently did they change jobs. This was also true the longer the period of time that had passed after they had left Northways.

In the first year of operation of the project the boys were unemployed for an average period of four weeks. This was higher in the second year, an average of eleven weeks, since the boys found it extremely difficult to obtain jobs during the recession period. The boys living in the unit took an average of two weeks longer to find a job after this than the boys who had left. Apart from periods of unemployment, absenteeism was also high; twenty-five days per year as an average per boy. This figure is enhanced because during the period of the project three highly disturbed boys had an average of seventy days absenteeism each.

It is clear from these figures that the boys did in fact act out their self-destructive wishes through their jobs. After our initial mistake about their rent they had to pay this, whether they were employed or not, so the job changeover, absenteeism, and unemployment were effectively weapons against themselves.

If the boys who left Northways had continued to change jobs at the same rate, even though they were not overtly delinquent, it would mean that the risk of breakdown in this way remained statistically very high. No boys have been away from Northways long enough to indicate more than a trend, but of the boys who have been away more than one year, at the time of writing, their job turnover has been reduced to an average of two to three per annum. Since over half this group are in the building trade, this would indicate a settling process.

The distribution of trades between the three groups two years after the start of the project in the height of the winter recession was as follows:

TABLE 7

	Northways	Ex-Northways	Homeless Control	Home Control
Unemployed	4	4	5	4
Labourers	1	4	12	13
Army	0	1	0	0
Trainee posts	2	0	0	0
Semi-skilled	0	1	3	1

The proportion of unemployed is high for the boys who lived or had lived in Northways. This is explicable, because both groups were living in the same district and were unwilling to move to look for jobs because of the protection they felt from the project. Considering the intelligence levels of the boys in all the groups, the number of unskilled labourers is higher than one would expect for this range in the community at large.

The pattern of job changing was not very successfully modified while the boys continued to live in Northways, but it tended not to persist, as we have said, after they left. We remained uncertain whether job shifting represented a part of their transitional difficulties in adapting to society, difficulties which in the control groups perhaps led to reconviction, or whether it was a symptom which became built into the way of life of the community before we were able to contain it. Another model of Northways would be needed to assess this.

CHAPTER XIII

The Aims of Diagnosis

THE JUSTIFICATION for the aetiological classification of delinquency given in the first chapter of this book is that it might make treatment attempts more rational and more economical of time and effort. As far as 'personality delinquency' is concerned, the assets, liabilities, and needs of individuals must be considered if treatment is to be successful.

If our results have any significance, they raise questions as to the use of predictive rating scales as, when is often the case, they are taken to indicate the likely fate of individuals. Although the Mannheim-Wilkins assessment of the boys is not a prediction for any one boy, it is often considered to indicate something of his chance of successful adjustment. Eighteen months after the start of the project those Northways boys who failed and were reconvicted showed a statistical score on the scale as follows: 72%, 70%, 49%, 27%, 24%, 15%. For one boy the figure was not worked out. The boys who had so far not been reconvicted, and had left Northways, had assessments as follows: 68%, 62%, 55%, 51%, 43%, 37%, 33%, 26%, 20%, 15%. These results would indicate that these assessments are not helpful in assessing the individual's chances of success if boys are placed in a therapeutic environment after discharge from borstal; nor do they then give any measure of the ultimate chances of successful adjustment for such boys in the community at large.

Success in Northways was independent of standard clinical diagnosis; one of the boys who failed was suffering from a schizophrenic reaction, so was one of the boys who succeeded and married. Neither was it related to duration of institutionalization. The boy who had the longest experience of this, fifteen years, had one reconviction for stealing from the warden, but, as we have said, he should not necessarily be considered a psychosocial failure. Failure, however, was related to two specific psychological facts; those boys who failed were unable to establish a relationship with an adult, they were so withdrawn or hyper-suspicious that the caring-for intentions of adults were internally distorted and perceived as persecuting, or they were so intolerant of separation that they could not contain their liability to act out their rage and despair on the community at large. Those boys who succeeded established a meaningful relationship with adults and were able to give up their basic suspiciousness in response to being cared for and to interpretations as to the 'hidden equations' behind their words or actions. Thus the actions and words of adults could be perceived as 'loving'. Consequently the boys became able to tolerate some anxiety about themselves and begin to contain their acting-out of conflicts.

It is noteworthy that the indications for success in the unit are the same as for a successful response to outpatient psychotherapy. Thus the response of a boy to an interpretation in the initial interview for Northways and his ability to establish a relationship with the interviewer can now be used as a predictive measure for success or failure in the project.

Of the boys who came to the unit only one might, in the present state of psychological knowledge, be considered untreatable given an optimum psychosocial environment, and these are some of the most disturbed of all the boys who enter the penal system.

It would appear that the aim of the diagnostic assessment should be to determine the points in the life of the individual at which therapy can be most efficaciously applied. The questions that need to be asked in 'situational delinquency' are whether the environment can be changed and, if not, whether the adolescent delinquent can be helped to resist its pressures. This may mean for the borstal boy no more than very adequate vocational training fitted to his abilities. Where 'intra-familial delinquency' is concerned the same type of question applies. For 'personality delinquency' our study would indicate that there is a place for the small institution, open to the community, created in the manner we have described. This cannot, however, possibly provide all the therapeutic resources that are needed for the various types of psychosocial disturbance.

The tendency in society at large is for small institutions to reject those individuals they feel they cannot treat. Such people then tend to move into non-therapeutic environments. In our experience severely disturbed antisocial personalities who are highly 'schizoid' require a therapeutic environment which it is not possible to leave. There are individuals who cannot contain anxiety without physical support. In other words, if they are put in a situation that will be experienced as frustrating, they have to act to try to alter it, even if the actions are highly antisocial. If these actions cannot be contained, such antisocial individuals do not experience the need for a human relationship, without which, we would hypothesize, psychosocial maturation is impossible. Thus the institutional treatment of delinquents in the larger sense requires facilities that can be, on the one hand, open to the community, with many community links, or, on the other, closed and secure. Since human beings who mature should become capable of handling frustrations and rejecting immediate gratifications at whatever future cost, it would appear that the ideal treatment institution requires both closed and open facilities to enable its inmates to keep the same therapeutic relationships throughout their stay. The idea of an institution that is either open or closed must inhibit the treatment of the more disturbed group of the 'delinquent' population.

The concept is reinforced by considering the results of treatment in an institution for delinquent boys aged from sixteen to nineteen.

It began to be revived in October 1959 from having been a rigid custodial setting. The results for the year July 1960–July 1961 show that, of eighty-two boys who left the school, only thirty-one (38%) have not been reconvicted after two years. The following year (1961–1962), with a maximum follow-up period of one year, out of eighty-eight boys discharged, forty-eight (54%) have made a successful adjustment.

On the face of it these results are not inspiring, even with the short time at risk, but this is a setting which does not, as yet, provide adequate work with the boys' families, nor does it receive adequate information about the type of sub-cultural environment from which the boys come. There is a routine of treatment which stresses a realistic approach to vocational training and social adjustment; it is, however, an open environment which depends for personality controls primarily on the relationships established between the boys and the staff and each other. When a boy first comes to the school a prediction is made by the senior staff concerning the likelihood that the boy's needs can be met by the total environment. With success arbitrarily defined in terms of the ability not to be reconvicted, the results show that, in the year 1960–1961, of forty-four boys who it was thought could respond to the routine environment of the school, twenty-four were not reconvicted at a two-year follow-up. In 1961–1962, with only a one-year follow-up, thirty-nine out of forty-seven boys were not reconvicted.

Other boys, within two to three weeks of admission, are considered to need both open and closed care, without necessarily any special additional psychotherapeutic measures. In other words, the assumption is that if they are to establish meaningful relationships with the staff, external control of their aggressive actions is necessary. The institution could not provide this control, and the results for the second group show that of fifteen boys in 1960–1961 thought to need this type of care and not able to obtain it in the setting, all were reconvicted after two years. Of twenty such boys the following year, at one year of follow-up, eighteen have been reconvicted.

Another group of boys were felt to be more severely disturbed 'personality delinquents'; they were mentally defective, suffered from severe character problems, or were psychotic. They were recommended for psychiatric hospitalization, in an adolescent

The Aims of Diagnosis

unit, a hospital for psychopaths or a mental deficiency hospital as appropriate. It is instructive to see what happened to the group for whom such places were not available.

A number were sent to various types of hospital, but in several cases boys were discharged because the hospital did not have the facilities for treating them. For the 1960–1961 figures one such boy out of five has not been reconvicted; for 1961–1962, two out of nine are still at liberty after one year.

TABLE 8 BOYS RECOMMENDED FOR PSYCHIATRIC HOSPITALIZATION AND NOT SENT

	Total	Number successful	Number Reconvicted Not further Institu- tionalized	Reinstitu- tionalized
1960–61	8	2	1	5
1961–62	6	0	0	6

As the therapeutic environment developed, psychotherapy was provided for some of those personality delinquents who, it was thought, might respond to the general milieu with the help of special psychotherapeutic intervention from a trained therapist. In 1960–1961, three out of five such boys were still at liberty; for the following year five out of six were similarly making a reasonable adjustment.

In 1960–1961 four boys were recommended for psychotherapy but did not receive it; three of them were reconvicted. Not all the boys felt to need closed-and-open care were seen by the psychiatrist, and it may be that some of these might, in fact, have carried a recommendation for psychiatric hospitalization or psychotherapeutic intervention.

These figures, along with the study of the failures of the Northways project, do not prove that adequate assessment, diagnosis, and treatment are necessary prerequisites for the successful psychosocial treatment of delinquency, but they do perhaps indicate that without these the results of treatment will continue to be inadequate.

Q

CHAPTER XIV

Summary

IN OUR opinion the project could not have had the measure of success it did if the larger society in which the boys were living had not provided jobs and if the house had been sited in a high-delinquency area. In other words, the rehabilitation of disturbed youth is ultimately possible only if the opportunities to be constructive are present and easily available in society. It is clear that the boys under our care would not have been able to support themselves without the assistance of a situation in which a variety of social services were easily accessible and job opportunities were present. If the community had been placed in an area of high unemployment, as events of the recession winter of 1962–1963 demonstrated, the group of boys would have lacked the capacity to cope with and compete in unfavourable conditions. Similarly, if the staff had not understood that the way of life of a working-class youth is different from that of the middle classes, the project might have collapsed. We understood, as was said in Chapter II, that a working-class boy might eat an evening meal in an under-shirt without being hostile, that washing-up was not an acceptable chore, and that it is sociologically aberrant for a working-class boy to do housework. The project might similarly have failed if the trustee group had been overtly interfering or, given that a need was demonstrably necessary, they had taken months to meet it with the consequent frustration of staff and boys.

Delinquency may be looked upon as the result of outwardly directed aggressive actions on the part of an individual which are rightly perceived by the society in which he lives as an attack.

212

Its aetiological roots are, as has been said, to be found in society, the family, and the individual. When a delinquent act occurs immediate pain is experienced by others rather than by the person committing the crime. To such disturbance society at large at first reacts by attempting to be helpful. This arouses in the delinquent intense mixed feelings, and his response is a greedy attack. This becomes intolerable, inevitably society becomes coercive, and a vicious circle of attack and coercive defence appears to be created. To the extent that disapproval is registered by specific punishment for a specific act, it is not necessarily unhelpful in that it is realistic; but it does not resolve the liability of disturbed people to commit further crimes, and may even enhance it. More serious from a prognostic viewpoint is the mutual withdrawal from each other of society and the attackers; it is as if society decides that conditions are irreversible, and the same deduction is made by the delinquent. This may account for the relative neglect that is ultimately shown by society to its delinquents, and for the attitude of delinquents that they themselves are not cared about.

Because the delinquency of the boys who came to Northways had not, we think, been adequately classified prior to their borstal sentence, psychological treatment had, in most cases, not been recognized as necessary. Diagnostically they might have been identified as primarily 'personality delinquents'; two-thirds of them being sufferers from character disorders, one-third having in addition the liability to schizophrenic reactions. Secondly, they were 'situational delinquents', in that, almost inevitably, without help they gravitated towards sub-sections of our society that accept antisocial behaviour as a way of life. Finally, they had recognizable institutional syndromes which were likely to be reinforced by further typical institutional living. Even if a diagnostic classification of delinquency were constructed differently, the failure to offer adequate treatment in more usual penal settings may primarily be a function of the shortage of psychiatrists and psychologists.

Antisocial behaviour may be said to appear as an attempt on the part of an individual to maintain a state of psychological equilibrium, in relation both to himself and to the objects in his environment, his external world. The act is a psychological attempt to balance oneself against the stresses and strains which play upon one from the outer and inner worlds and to avoid tension states.

Thus the goal of treatment should be to help the individual so that he may tolerate frustration without reacting in an aggressively destructive manner either towards the self or towards others. In this process a capacity to consider the feelings of others needs to be acquired, as well as an ability accurately to appraise reality. This means that institutions that treat delinquents should be well aware of social norms, and should understand the implications for the individual of creating a social system that is, in terms of society at large, a social aberration. Any institution, penal or otherwise, which does not help to create a firm feeling of social, psychological, and economic identity is unlikely to help other than situational, some intra-familial, and the transient personality types of delinquency.

We believe that the human misfits who are our institutionalized delinquents can be salvaged if the people who are attempting to be helpful really demonstrate that they care about them. This is not inconsistent with a psychotherapeutic approach that interprets aggressive feelings, and, in fact, the more one demonstrates 'love' in action the more necessary is it, with boys suffering from severely disturbed character disorders, to recognize their hate and interpret it. It is not helpful for psychotherapeutic personnel to become the patients' doormats upon which they wipe their emotionally dirty feet. Nor should personnel ever be manoeuvred into a situation in which they appear to the delinquent to be colluding in an antisocial act. In our opinion, the problem of the delinquent characters we have described can be resolved only if their communication difficulties are understood and actions are recognized as being highly meaningful to them.

It may well be that if our project is ultimately as significant as our results so far indicate, one crucial factor may prove to be that the main 'authority' figure in the house was a woman who was neither coercive nor emotionally depriving and that the balancing male figure was a psychiatrist. This is not to underestimate the importance of the other people in the team and of the social factors we have described, but if this hypothesis is valid, institutions for disturbed male adolescents should have many more significant women in their social systems. This is certainly true for institutions concerned with the classical forms of mental illness and is perhaps as valid for those dealing with severe character problems.

It is difficult to know how coercive techniques, which continue to be used, can be helpful in promoting personality growth. In some countries institutions still exist which perpetuate a system in which the inmates are supposed not to talk to each other for weeks or months and in which dietary punishments and isolation techniques are often used. Despite this extreme rigidity, or perhaps because of it, control is such that it is still possible for a 'daddy' system to exist, on the basis not of tobacco, but of the 'respect' that must be shown by new inmates to older ones; this is enforced by physical violence.

One therapeutic technique that has been devised in an attempt to get away from the difficulties created by large, hierarchical 'custodial' settings is the small residential institution for disturbed youth. Two recent British publications[1] discuss variations of this model applied to children below school-leaving age. Both report experiments that failed, in that the institutions they describe were closed down by the relevant authorities. They discuss attempts to be helpful to individuals, but the type of mal-adjustment for which the children were sent to them in the first place is unclear. In the one, a combination of a therapeutic school milieu and individual psychotherapy was offered for some of the youngsters; in the other, the main treatment device appears to have been the use of group processes. Although, of necessity, neither of these could be controlled studies, it would appear that

---

[1] Shields, R. W. *A Cure of Delinquents*. London: Heinemann, 1962.
Jones, H. *Reluctant Rebels*. London: Tavistock Publications, 1960; New York: Association Press.

both produced helpful results in a significant proportion of their charges. It is unfortunate that neither makes clear why society found them intolerable burdens. It is not sociologically valid for the therapeutic institution as a whole to project the responsibility for failure onto bad authority figures. This attitude, which is overt in one of these studies, usually represents a defensive manoeuvre on the part of the total institution. The present project continues with no apparent likelihood of being closed.

Another experimental approach, again using group relationships, is the short stay 'Highfields'[2] project in the United States. An account is given of 'Group Interaction', a procedure in which the young people meet with the therapist-administrator five times weekly with the goal of acquiring 'peer group insight' and ventilating feelings and hostility. Positive results of this project are described, but it is difficult to discern exactly what types of personality were admitted.

All attacks on society are not necessarily performed by disturbed people. It is, however, not unreasonable to hypothesize that if these acts continue, one should consider not only the individual performing them but also the society in which he lives. If, in an institution, there is an outbreak of disturbed behaviour, it is highly probable that there is something amiss in the total institutional system. If there is no resolution of the conflicts in the latter, punishment of the delinquents will, if it is severe enough, drive the tension underground; it will not resolve the propensity for another type of outbreak to occur.

The Northways experiment did not attempt to drive tensions underground, nor, on the other hand, did it consciously attempt to provoke their expression. When tension-driven impulsive behaviour appeared, it was, so far as possible, contained by verbal control in an interpersonal situation, without the use of threats and with interpretative comments as to its meaning in the present life-situation of the individual. As the project developed, subtle controls were built into the social system, so that, after two years, 'decency' was more and more part of the way of life of the house

[2] Weeks, H. A. *Youthful Offenders at Highfields.* University of Michigan Press, 1958.

which had become a home. Violence was not used, and inappropriate sexuality was contained. Consideration for others became so much more the norm that the boys began to take responsibility for getting each other up in the morning and they were able to ensure that one of their number who had a gastric ulcer, and was inclined to hurt himself by taking the occasional glass of alcohol, did not do so.

Control is best produced in meaningful interpersonal situations. Specific punishment has probably no effect on disturbed adults; for adolescents it may be a necessary way of demonstrating to an individual the reality that society disapproves of a particular action. It is, however, sterile unless the punisher is admired and respected by the person punished. Punishment was never used in the Northways project. If controls for an individual cannot be established with interpersonal and intra-group relationships, then external controls through physical structure, in terms either of a building or of people, are necessary. External controls should neither be excessive, because then they are infantilizing and make for undue dependence, nor should they be inadequate, because this can be frightening, and the individual then reacts in such a way as implicitly to ask for more control.

The essence of treatment for the disturbed individual is to create a situation in which he feels loved, his aggressive feelings and the anxiety associated with them are understood, and the outward expression in action of destructive aggression is controlled. One skill in treating such an individual lies in judging the amount of responsibility he is able to handle. Disturbance in a personality needs to be therapeutically resolved in one-to-one interpersonal situations, in intra-group situations, and in relationship to society at large. In addition, a human being requires the opportunity to be constructive to the maximum of his own capabilities; neither more nor less should be expected of him. Finally it is necessary to recognize basic human needs. One that is particularly relevant with male adolescents, is to feel that one can successfully defy authority and thus assert one's masculinity. This need is frustrated when parents and treatment settings do not fix limits that allow their charges the opportunity to defy them without hurting either themselves or society; or, when they offer so much understanding that the adolescent is made impotent; or when they are too restrictive.

These are the principles on which we created Northways, and they perhaps apply to all therapeutic environments.

One aspect of the treatment described in Northways, the careful working out of the separation anxiety experienced by the boys when they left, is of particular relevance. If the general tension that we observed surrounding the departure of any one boy occurs in all institutional situations in which boys are able to make relationships, we would surmise that this is of particular importance in other such settings. It also appears from the project that staff can be trained to be more adequate therapeutic personnel without making them inhibited and anxious as people.

The Northways type of setting appears to improve the psycho-social adjustment of young men aged seventeen to twenty-one of average intelligence who are able to establish some relationships with adults. We would hesitate to assert that these boys are cured, but within the period under review, two and a half years, which is not yet long enough to be statistically valid, the recidivist rate of the group was considerably less than might otherwise have been expected.

Northways is only one kind of model, and people who are highly 'schizoid' or who cannot tolerate the frustration involved in separation without attacking the community at large do not do well there. If people are not in these categories it may be that they can be helped in equivalent types of community, but since some of their basic characteristics are different the techniques would have to be modified. If the age group was younger, say thirteen to sixteen, it is clear that the 'rules' of the house would have to be different. We would not, for example, put disturbed boys in early adolescence in double rooms if only because this is an age at which mutual sexual exploration is not uncommon in our society. We would not give them door keys or allow them to be out late at night. The relationship to money and to the staff would be quite changed, and the wardens' roles would be more realistically parental. If such a community was created for girls of the same age group we would provide them with individual bed-sitting rooms; girls do not naturally form large group relationships. If the girls' disturbance showed in promiscuous behaviour we doubt that a small community could have been found in which this did not occur. This clearly would influence larger community relationships. For a group of higher intelligence, but equally disturbed, more individual therapy would perhaps be necessary. Alternatively, if the group was of borderline intelligence, a simpler social structure might be desirable.

Cultural differences between adolescents, both in the same society and in different countries, are relevant, just as are the cultural differences in the community at large. If these are taken into account it is likely that Northways is a repeatable model both nationally and internationally. For example, the fundamental intrapsychic difficulties among American and British adolescents are not, in this author's experience, too different, although as a gross clinical generalization it may be said that the American adolescent is likely to be more overtly aggressive and more anxious about homosexuality than his British counterpart. On the other hand, it would appear that the fundamental depression of the disturbed delinquent adolescent is more easily accessible to therapy in Britain.

There are some 'hostels' in which all age-groups and all types of clinical problem are admitted and in which the physical standards are often quite low. We would regard these as providing an environment in which secure, socially acceptable identifications are almost impossible for adolescents to achieve.

It would appear that the project described might justify the creation of more pilot models on similar lines. We do not believe that its apparent 'success' is a function of a special unrepeatable capacity of the people involved, and from a replication of this idea more might be learned about the value of a therapeutic 'home' environment as compared with a more typical institutional setting. The techniques required to offer the floundering aggressive human beings we have described a lifeline to be a better and more socially rewarding and acceptable life need, in a similar way, to be refined and better understood.

If a project is successful the cost to the community in economic terms is important and should not be neglected. It is reasonable to assess that every year a human being spends in a typical institution costs the state a minimum of £500,[3] apart from the fact that such human beings are producing nothing of value to the community. If a homeless boy has been in institutions for ten years he has cost the community about £5,000, at a minimum. Thus the whole Northways group had cost about £100,000 prior to their arrival. The cost of the rehabilitation of each boy in Northways was approximately £500, excluding the amortization of the cost of the building, but including replacement of equipment, decoration, and so on. Apart from the grief and suffering that was abated for the boys and the community, this would appear to be an economically sound proposition. Furthermore the boys were being reasonably productive members of the community in that for a significant period of each year they were working.

It would appear that the unit justified its existence in both human and economic terms: homeless human beings developed a capacity to make homes for themselves, and the cost to the community in real expenditure as well as in protection from aggressive attack was considerably reduced.

[3] The average annual cost per inmate for all types of penal establishment is £520. Report of the Commissioners of Prisons. London: H.M.S.O., 1962.

INDEX

absenteeism, 205
accidents, 175
adolescence, 7f; family background and, 111f
aetiology, 2ff
after-care problem, 8
age: on admission, 19; of residents, average, 180
aggression, 11, 84f; change in object, 173f; constructive use of, 126; control of, 68; theft as, 171
aims: of experiment, 100; of treatment, 214
alcoholism, 181
anger, need to avoid, 91
anxiety, 39; paranoid, 84, 188; *see also* separation
appearance, external, of house, 36
approved schools, 97f, 201
'as if' personality, 109
assault, 96; *see also* violence
assessment: diagnostic, aim of, 208; initial, 26f
assessments, and borstal records, compared, 105ff
authority figures: attitude to, 133; difficulties with, 75

bedrooms, 47
behaviour, and social environment, 13
behaviour problems, 22f
'black-outs', 109
borderline psychotics, 24
borrowing, 73
borstal: desire to return to, xiii; procedure on discharge, 15; psychiatric treatment in, 203; recalls to, 195f; staff, relation to, 68f
brain change, organic, 4
building, description of, 46

catatonia, 64
character disorder, 4
charitable efforts, 11
child guidance clinic, 7
children, attitude to, 182
chlorpromazine, 13n
class, social, 21, 212
cleaners, attitude to, 51
cleanliness, 76
clothing, and borstal discharge, 71

coercion, value of, 215
cohesion, group, 170
collusion, 154
committee, house, x
communication, 41, 214
community, local, relations with, 36f
concentration camps, 12
confidentiality, 29, 60, 154
confusional behaviour, 24
conscience, reinforcing, 5, 10
consideration for others, 169f, 217
consistency, of outer world, 54
control, rigid, effects of, 113
control group, 31ff, 41; comparison of, 195ff
controls: external, 217; operation of, 114ff, 132
cook, attitude to, 51
costs, of Northways, 220
counselling, 140; *see also* group counselling
crime(s): character of, 95ff, 198; relation to personality, 95f

'daddy system', 70
death, parental, 4f
'decency', 216
defences/defence mechanisms, 10, 80, 87, 92
deficiency disease, emotional, 6
delinquents, classification, 2ff
delusional behaviour, 24
denial, 80, 101
depersonalization, 26
depressed reactions/depression, 64, 101, 102
deprivation: emotional, effects, 78ff; maternal, 80
destructiveness, 172
detention centres, 136
deterrence, borstal and, 67
diagnosis: attitudes to, 5f; and success, 207
Director of Borstal After-Care, 40f, 155, 162, 164
drugs, 7, 178
duration of stay, 9

ego: controls, 10; strength, and transference neurosis, 137; structure, 10
emotional disturbance, degree of, 100
emotional trauma, 4
employers, relations with, 43ff

221

Index

employment: exchange, 38; officer, 38; record, 98f
enuresis, 24
environment, permissive and punitive, 11f
environmental factors, 2f
envy, 80; of female productivity, 177
equilibrium, psychological, 214
experience, learning from, 102

failures, causes of, 184ff
family: background, desirable, 111f; breakdown, results, 6; conflicts within, 3f
fathers, as identification figures, 174
flat, staff, 47
food: arrangements, 46f, 160, 178; budget, 178; greed for, 169
foster-children, 6
friendships, with delinquents, 166
frustration, reaction to, 84
furniture, 46, 159, 172

gambling, compulsive, 85
garden, 47, 73
getting up, difficulties, 55, 75
girls: and group relationships, 135; relations with, 76, 82f
girl-friends: as fantasy projections, 83f; rejection by, effects, 174; relation to warden, 53; violence towards, 83; as visitors to house, 165
glasses, 76
'good', institutional and social, 114
group contagion, 3, 95
group counselling, xvi, xxii, 69
'group interaction', 216
group processes, 134ff; operation of, 148; training for, 136; value of, 135
group therapy: functioning of, 138; optimum size for, 141; supportive and expressive, 140
growth problems, 4
guests, 165f
guilt: absence of, 67; expiation of, 4f

haircutting, 72
heat, liking for, 94
heating, 47f
help, desire for, expressed in behaviour, 102
'Highfields' project, 216
hire-purchase, 159
history, past, concealment of, 66
home, hostel as, xvii, xxiif
homes, of ex-Northways boys, 182
homosexuality, 129f; overt, 23
hospitals, 38

hostel: associations of name, 48; features of desirable, xviff
housebreaking, 87
housemasters, borstal, attitude to, 67
house meetings, see meetings
hyper-morality, 12
hypochondria, 85, 92

identification, 12, 105, 113; control by, 175
identity: problems of, 23, 71, 92; wish for new, 16
illness, 4, 175f
improvement, assessment of, 173
India, 2
infantilization, 160
institutional experience, previous, 97f
institutionalization: average period, 20, 98; length of, and reconviction, 203; effects, 6ff, 65ff
institutions, open and closed, 209
Insurance, National, 44
intellectual ability, 21f
I.Q., 22, 88
intelligence tests, 29
internalization, of difficulties, 113
interpretation(s): expressive, 40; need of, 68; response to, 102; supportive, 139; transference, 138; utility of, in adolescence, 113
intra-familial delinquency, 3f, 208
isolation, 80

jealousy, 82
job: instability, 20; reactions on loss of, 72f; turnover, 98f, 203f
Jones, Maxwell, 136

keys, 167

language, institutional, 66
laundry, 47
leaving: freedom of, 15; as sanction, 156
leisure activities, 56, 76
light, dislike of, 94
loan fund, 40, 158f
location of house, 35f
love, lack of, 93

manipulation, attempts at, 56, 153, 161
Mannheim-Wilkins assessment, 25, 207
marriage: attitude to, 76f; of Northways boys, 182
masculinity: assertion of, and dress, 72; valuation of, 21, 56f; see also identity
matching, of controls, 32f
material assistance, provision for, 40
maturity, psychosocial, xxiv
mechanization, industrial, 44, 70

222

Index